Expressions From Southern Scotland

Edited by Samantha Wood

First published in Great Britain in 2010 by

Remus House
Coltsfoot Drive
Peterborough
PE2 9JX
Telephone: 01733 890066
Website: www.youngwriters.co.uk

Book Design by Spencer Hart

SB ISBN 978-1-84924-788-7

Foreword

At Young Writers our defining aim is to promote an enjoyment of reading and writing amongst children and young adults. By giving aspiring poets the opportunity to see their work in print, their love of the written word as well as confidence in their own abilities has the chance to blossom.

Our latest competition Poetry Explorers was designed to introduce primary school children to the wonders of creative expression. They were given free reign to write on any theme and in any style, thus encouraging them to use and explore a variety of different poetic forms.

We are proud to present the resulting collection of regional anthologies which are an excellent showcase of young writing talent. With such a diverse range of entries received, the selection process was difficult yet very rewarding. From comical rhymes to poignant verses, there is plenty to entertain and inspire within these pages. We hope you agree that this collection bursting with imagination is one to treasure.

Contents

Oxgangs Primary School, Edinburgh

Riverside Primary School, Stirling

St Andrew's Primary School, Falkirk

St Francis Xavier's Primary School, Falkirk

St Ninian's RC Primary School, Cardenden

The Poems

Minstrel

My pony, called Minstrel,
He's lots of fun,
We could play all day,
In the winter's chill or the summer's sun.

My feet in the stirrups,
With a squeeze, we walk,
His swishes his tail,
His ears turn to listen, when I talk.

As I grip the reins,
The air is cold,
Another squeeze, we trot,
I feel so bold.

The noise of his hooves,
As we go through the paces,
The wind in my hair,
My heart races.

Faster, faster,
Let's canter!

Emma McGraw (10)

Exploring Space

Planets spinning,
Earth winning,
Neptune crossing,
Pluto bossing,
Big holes,
Tiny coals,
Saturn's loop,
Jupiter's hoop,
Mercury napped,
Mars attacks!

Aurora Bruce (8)
Barshare Primary School, Cumnock

Space

Human rocket,
Shuttles shaking,
Burning, turning,
Shouting, routing!
Space nearer,
Planet keeper,
Alien sleeper,
Stars flashing,
Sun brightening,
Zero gravity.

Aiden McGregor (9)
Barshare Primary School, Cumnock

The Planets

Planets spinning
Colours swirling
Rings twirling
Gases moving
Hot air blowing
Astronauts exploring
Looking, picturing
Air suit breathing
Tanks helping
Beautiful planets.

Robert Marshall (9)
Barshare Primary School, Cumnock

Shooting Star

No life
Nothing on it
Planets floating
Tail comet.

Connor Gugliemucci (8)
Barshare Primary School, Cumnock

The Moon

Night shiner
Rocky surface
Night light
Bright half
Silver ball
Rocky craters
Shining bright
Spinning sphere
Floating ball.

Alison Farrell (8)
Barshare Primary School, Cumnock

The Sun

The sun, high in the sky
Planets spinning around
Mercury - closest to the sun
Pluto's last, way down
Rockets flying by
Spacemen exploring
Planets . . .
High in the night sky.

Megan Dickson (8)
Barshare Primary School, Cumnock

Moon

Spinning planet
Night giver
Dark object
Frost maker
Ice bringer
Winter changer
Orbit machine.

Austin McBurnie I8)
Barshare Primary School, Cumnock

Space

Rockets blasting
Stars shooting
Saturn turning
Sun shining
The moonlight
Earth spinning
Through the night.

Morgan McLean (9)
Barshare Primary School, Cumnock

Rocket

Launching off
Fire blasting
Sharp point
Launch pad
Blast off
Zooming in
Rocket fuel.

Nia Lowe (9)
Barshare Primary School, Cumnock

Outer Space

Fiery ball
Sparkly dust
Silent, dark
White shapely globe
Big dipper
Milky Way.

Chloe Ponton (9)
Barshare Primary School, Cumnock

Space

Starry night
Dark sky
Shooting stars
Crescent moon
No oxygen
Nothing living.

Daniel Girvan (8)
Barshare Primary School, Cumnock

Blasting Off

Rip roaring
Engine blasting
Flame throwing
Space soaring
Moon landing
Men exploring.

Chloe Paterson (9)
Barshare Primary School, Cumnock

Space

Twinkling stars
Cold air
Darkness everywhere
Blasting rockets
Bumpy ground
Exploring everywhere.

Caitlin McGinn (9)
Barshare Primary School, Cumnock

Planet Mars

A red ball.
A slow mover.
A rocket planet.
A non-living place.
A great canyon.

Jamie Montgomery (8)
Barshare Primary School, Cumnock

Venus

Cloud surrounded
Outer space
Hottest planet
Unknown colour
Size of Earth.

Zak Donald (9)
Barshare Primary School, Cumnock

My Dreams

When I dream I think of things
No one would ever know
Like a pig dancing
Or a kangaroo on snow.

Jelly beans in custard
Would be beans on toast
Snowboarding on trampolines
Is what I like the most.

So my world is magical
As magical as can be
I call this world Utopia
It's magical to me!

Megan Grant (10)
Davidson's Mains Primary School, Edinburgh

A Very Random Senses Poem

I saw a black cat as black as the ocean at night.
I saw a young man as mad as a hatter.
I saw a puppy as fierce as a lion.

I heard the wind as fierce as the sun's blaze.
I heard a faint cry from a man as poor as a church mouse.
I heard her voice as clear as a whistle.
I heard the girl sing as sweet as honey from a hive.

I felt the ghost's cold touch as cold as frostbite.
I felt the warm coat as warm as wool.
I felt the dog's ears as soft as silk.

I smelt the gas as strong as a horse.
I smelt a rose as red as blood.
I smelt the smoke as bold as brass.
I smelt a daffodil as yellow as a banana.

I tasted a peach as good as gold.
I tasted a lemon as bitter as vinegar.
I tasted a strawberry as red as a rose.
I tasted a banana as yellow as a chick.

Rhiann Hart (10)
Davidson's Mains Primary School, Edinburgh

Who Is This?

Who looks like a rock when it hides away?
Who is faster than people say?
Who gets put away in the winter?

Who loves the sun?
Who can be big or small?
Who loves to eat?

Is it a monkey, a lion, a crab,
A spider, a panda, a koala?
No! It's a tortoise!

Lauryn Arthur (10)
Davidson's Mains Primary School, Edinburgh

Wonderful World

I can see . . .
Bare trees and waving grass
The blinding sun and the cloudy sky

I can taste . . .
Heavenly chocolate ice cream
Mouth-watering apple pie

I can hear . . .
Cheerful music, joyful laughter
Lovely words you said!

I can smell . . .
Sweet perfume, colourful flowers
Freshly baked bread

I can touch . . .
Smooth silk, expensive velvet
A cute baby's skin

What a joyful world I'm in!

Rebecca Lawrence (10)
Davidson's Mains Primary School, Edinburgh

The Dog

Who barks in the park,
Chases cats at night,
Gives them a fright?

Who creates mayhem,
Raids through bins,
Finds lots of tins?

Who jumps on the table,
Steals our food?
Mmmm, tastes good.

It's a dog.

Lewis Harrison (9)
Davidson's Mains Primary School, Edinburgh

Wonderful World

I can see . . .
Lofty trees and swaying grass
The blinding sun and clear sky

I can taste . . .
Tasty chocolate, freezing ice cream
Mouth-watering apple pie

I can hear . . .
Blaring music, infectious laughter
Peaceful words you said

I can smell . . .
Scented perfume, strong flowers
Delicious baking bread

I can touch . . .
Delicate silk and glistening velvet
Smooth as a baby's skin

What a wonderful, amazing world I'm in.

Ronan Wood (9)
Davidson's Mains Primary School, Edinburgh

The Eagle

Who swoops and dives,
Soars through the skies?

Who nests in trees,
Away from you and me?

Who fishes in long-lost lakes,
Where no one has ever been?

Who can fly fifty miles,
With no breaks?

The eagle.

Joseph Lucey (10)
Davidson's Mains Primary School, Edinburgh

Wonderful World

I can see . . .
Lofty trees and gorgeous grass
A blinding sun and a beautiful sky

I can taste . . .
Scrumptious, freezing chocolate ice cream
And tempting apple pie

I can hear . . .
Booming music and cheerful laughter
Exciting words you said

I can smell . . .
Sweet perfume and delicate flowers
And attractive baking bread.

I can touch . . .
Soft silk and smooth velvet
And tender baby's skin

What a brilliant, wonderful world I'm in.

Ethan William Anderson (10)
Davidson's Mains Primary School, Edinburgh

What?

What tastes of chocolate melting in your mouth?
Galaxy, Yorkie or Aero sliding down your throat.

What's a pleasure to have?
Comfort, family and friends instead.

What makes a family special?
Love, joy and laughter.

What keeps you going even when you're sad?
Knowing that someone's there for you no matter what you do.

Mairi Guild (10)
Davidson's Mains Primary School, Edinburgh

Seasons

Amazingly cold
Extremely slippery
Incredibly nippy
Fantastically white

Childishly warm
Gloriously sunny
Understandingly bright
Strongly colourful

Unquestionably crisp
Stunningly drizzly
Beautifully golden
Happily colourful

Questionably dry
Joyfully happy
Comfortably pleasant
Famously beautiful.

Christy Guild (10)
Davidson's Mains Primary School, Edinburgh

Hallowe'en

H ats and masks make you scared.
A ll the ghouls having a laugh.
L anterns flying through the air.
L eprechauns running down the streets.
O n-off, on-off go the lights in the haunted house.
W itches flying through the air on broomsticks.
E veryone trick or treating.
E choes of ghosts in the air.
N eighbourhoods filled with ghosts and ghouls.

Sophie Ross (10)
Davidson's Mains Primary School, Edinburgh

My Truly Fantastic Dog Poppy

Extremely cute
Humorously funny
Enormously loveable
Unimaginably sweet

Remarkably popular
Greatly sunny natured
Terribly jumpy
Truly excitable

Highly energetic
Acutely fun
Unusually strange
Uncommonly different

Tremendously boisterous
Strangely strong
Sometimes annoying.

Emma Gray (10)
Davidson's Mains Primary School, Edinburgh

September

Sun in September means warmth
Yellow, orange and red leaves
Shines with a golden light
Makes me happy

Wind is wild and noisy
Blows the leaves forward and backwards
Whistles through the trees
Makes me scared

Rain pouring down, making puddles
Running down the gutter like a river
Splashing people passing
Makes me wet.

Katie Parnell (10)
Davidson's Mains Primary School, Edinburgh

The Pokémon

Who swims in the frozen sea,
Much faster than you or me?
With the water in his eyes,
The sea is his disguise,
At the bottom of the ocean he lies.

He waits for his slippery prey,
I just want to say,
He can catch sixty fish in one day,
He does it the penguin way.

Have you any idea who he is?
If he was in mountain fizz,
He'd be so happy,
His wings would be flappy,
But not if you call him Snappy!
He's a Prinplup, the penguin Pokémon!

Jack Rawlinson (10)
Davidson's Mains Primary School, Edinburgh

The Honest Person

Incredibly kind
Truly honest
Pretty beautiful
Happiness sweet

Co-operative, protective
Pleasantly charming
Enjoyable person
Nicely polite

Careful children
Exciting journey
Good behaviour
Ticklishly humorous.

Phoebe Leong (10)
Davidson's Mains Primary School, Edinburgh

War

Walking the horrid wreckage
Gunshots went off
Absolutely devastated
'Never give up lads!'
But screams of horror
Explosions from the enemy
Enough is enough
Go out and fight
Deep into the night.

Jack Wood (10)
Davidson's Mains Primary School, Edinburgh

My Hamsters

Extremely cute,
Fantastically soft,
Amazingly furry,
Consistently jumpy.

Undoubtedly hyper,
Lovingly unique,
Tremendously little,
Sadly smelly.

Victoria Rudden (10)
Davidson's Mains Primary School, Edinburgh

My Favourite Colour

Y olk and exciting, always bright.
E xcellent and happy, always hyper.
L uminous and bright, always so yellow.
L oved and cared, always a star.
O utstanding and joyful, always standing out.
W onderful and warm, always by my side.

Alice Walker Stewart (10)
Davidson's Mains Primary School, Edinburgh

A Peaceful World

A cat was crawling silently to pounce on its prey, hungry for victory
An owl watching tentatively while eating his morning
Breakfast, roasted mice
Waves not so far away, crashing violently onto the shore
The monkey puzzle tree swaying gently in the wind
A drip, drops of snow as if there were white cushions everywhere
The rose which has come up went down
Into the ground again, shivering.

Rhona Fraser (10)
Davidson's Mains Primary School, Edinburgh

Peace

A fluffy rabbit hopping merrily in the field
A waterfall gushing down, glistening in the light
A penguin waddling silently in the cold white snow
A willow tree swaying in the breeze
The sun beating down endlessly from the clear blue sky
A red rose with petals slowly dropping off in the wind
The memories of all the good times friends have together
The love and fondness of your close family.

Emma Sunter (10)
Davidson's Mains Primary School, Edinburgh

Nature

Who can eat bamboo?
Not me or you.
Who can climb up high
Up to the sky?
Who is black and white?
Whose claws are very tight?
It's a panda don't you see?
This is nature for me.

Sean-Paul Scott (9)
Davidson's Mains Primary School, Edinburgh

My Cat

S elf confident, always guarding the house if another cat comes into the garden.
C razy, always making me laugh.
R ugged, looks like a big fluffy ball.
U nbelievable, always trying to eat our food!
F luffy and cuddly.
F un, always there to cheer me up.
Y oung at heart and energetic all the time.

Aisha Parker-Knowles (10)
Davidson's Mains Primary School, Edinburgh

Dedication For Windows

C ore 2 Duo, Intel powered.
O ne of your best friends.
M alicious at errors.
P eople cracking codes,
U nder spyware, Trojans and google.com.
T he AVG can't ever stop them!
E ndless hackers, hacked Darren Brown's site.
R eviewing Windows XP, Vista, 98, 95, Millennium Edition.

Nikolas Zakrzewski (10)
Davidson's Mains Primary School, Edinburgh

Hallowe'en

The ghost was as white as a sheet
The cat was as black as coal
The pumpkin was as bright as a light
The witch was as evil as a devil

The sky was as black as soot
The bat was as light as feathers
The skeleton was as old as the hills.

Amy Catherine Hailstones (10)
Davidson's Mains Primary School, Edinburgh

Hairy Fluff Balls

H airy and wild, a little coloured fluff ball.
A crobatic superstar, climbing up the cage.
M ischevious and sneaky, always wears a smile.
S leeping all the time, as cute as a puppy.
T roublesome when they bite you, lurking in the sawdust.
E nergetic and playful, always spinning in his wheel.
R avenous and starving, always wanting more food!

Ross Witney-Hunter (10)
Davidson's Mains Primary School, Edinburgh

Tynie

T ynie, fun loving and white.
Y ou would want him, because of his soft fur.
N aughty, jumping into other people's gardens.
I n seconds most of his bones are gone, sad eyes to say
'It wasn't me'.
E nergetic and strong, you would not like him running
towards you!

Courtney Tillbrook (10)
Davidson's Mains Primary School, Edinburgh

Hallowe'en

The bat was as black as coal
The witch's face was as green as grass
The ghost was as white as snow
The pumpkin was as heavy as an elephant
The skeleton was as old as the hills
The sky was as black as soot.

Amy Johnston (10)
Davidson's Mains Primary School, Edinburgh

Easter

E xciting
A mazing
S weet, sticky caramel
T ormenting chocolate comes your way
E aster bunnies hop
R oaming around the fields delivering eggs!

Bethan Jones (10)
Davidson's Mains Primary School, Edinburgh

My Favourite Animal

M ischievous all the time.
O range with a bit of brown.
N aughty but clever too.
K ing of the trees.
E nergetic and fun.
Y oung at heart all the time!

James Walter Paterson (10)
Davidson's Mains Primary School, Edinburgh

The Senses

I saw a rainbow as colourful as a parrot's tail.
I heard a ghost as terrifying as a clown.
I tasted cream as soft and slimy as a slug.
I smelled a lovely Galaxy as caramely as a cookie.
I touched a kitten's tail as soft as a feather.
I felt a fiery engine as hot as toast.

Nathan Kerr (10)
Davidson's Mains Primary School, Edinburgh

My Favourite Friend

S miley and happy, always funny.
O verjoyed, friend of a lifetime, always fun to be with.
P erfect for someone who wants to laugh, always kind.
H ighly hilarious, always seems delighted.
I ndependent, always a good friend to have.
E nthusiastic, always caring for the environment.

Fleur Demarlier (10)
Davidson's Mains Primary School, Edinburgh

Bonnie

B eautiful as gold.
O utside together we love to play.
N oisy and barking when a car door closes.
N ice when she's in a playful mood.
I ncredible, always running up and down,
E ntertaining me all the way throughout the day.

Tara Ramsay (10)
Davidson's Mains Primary School, Edinburgh

Hungry Jack

There was a boy called Jack
Who decided to have a snack
He looked and looked
Though his mummy cooked
He found a refreshing Tic Tac.

Afzal Miah (10)
Davidson's Mains Primary School, Edinburgh

Jack

There once was a boy called Jack
Who stood on a Tic Tac
He screamed and yelled
Sobbed and fell
And that was the end of that.

Michael Bowen (9)
Davidson's Mains Primary School, Edinburgh

The Bill

There once was a woman called Jill
Who forgot to pay her bill
She had a terrible fright
And out went the light
So she yelled for her husband, Phil.

Jamie Crozier (10)
Davidson's Mains Primary School, Edinburgh

The Fat Cat

There was a young girl with a cat.
She wanted to learn how to pat.
The cat ate a fox,
With a very big box,
And now the cat has got fat.

Eva Silverston (10)
Davidson's Mains Primary School, Edinburgh

My Best Friend

E xcellent and fearless, never scared of anything.
V ery funny, always making me laugh.
A mazing and cheerful, always chatting away.

Lauryn Leslie (9)
Davidson's Mains Primary School, Edinburgh

Glued To A Log

There was an old man with a dog,
That glued him to a log,
He stayed there all winter,
Then got a splinter,
And then he got stuck in a bog!

Nicole Aittahar (9)
Davidson's Mains Primary School, Edinburgh

An Important Animal

D arling when you're sitting in the sun.
A dorable little monster when you nibble my clothes.
I mpatient when you are waiting for your food.
S tarry brown eyes, make me feel happy.
Y our furry ears relax when I stroke them.

Megan Boner (9)
Davidson's Mains Primary School, Edinburgh

The Man With Bread

There was a man with bread,
He wanted to lose his head.
He fell down a tunnel,
Got stuck in a funnel
And went to sleep in his bed.

Andrew Ellis (9)
Davidson's Mains Primary School, Edinburgh

The Shark In The Sea

I came to a restaurant for tea
I had a beautiful view of the sea
A shark came out
Then gave a big shout
'Why don't you come home with me?'

Analisa Love (10)
Davidson's Mains Primary School, Edinburgh

The Man With The Flute

There was an old man with a flute
Who wanted to know how to toot.
He tried and tried,
Until he died,
Then his girlfriend put on his suit.

Cora Todd (10)
Davidson's Mains Primary School, Edinburgh

Frankenstein's Bad Day

Frankenstein the monster was dead.
He was lying and crying in his bed.
Then he woke up
And found a cup
And unfortunately hurt his head.

Daniel Livingstone (9)
Davidson's Mains Primary School, Edinburgh

A Super Random Simile Poem

I heard a sound as loud as a sonic boom.
I saw a huge dragon as huge as a giant.
I felt as happy as a bird soaring through the Grand Canyon.
I touched a cloud as wet as Niagara Falls.
I smelled a lemon as sour as lime.

Melvin Abraham (10)
Davidson's Mains Primary School, Edinburgh

The Man With The Flu

There was an old man with the flu.
He accidentally stepped in some glue.
He made a big sneeze,
Which created a breeze,
That blew him into some stew!

Jack Miller (9)
Davidson's Mains Primary School, Edinburgh

Golf Is Fun

G ood for everyone.
O ver the hills you play.
L akes and rivers all over the place.
F orever and ever you play.

Kim Alison Paton (10)
Davidson's Mains Primary School, Edinburgh

An Important Animal

L ittle and energetic, always running around.
U sually mischievous, always stealing food.
C razy and silky, always by my side.
Y oung and silly, always by my side.

Alexander Cowan (10)
Davidson's Mains Primary School, Edinburgh

Terror

Terror is black, like an eternity of darkness
Terror is red, like the blood from a terrifying gash
Terror looks like a massive monster, devouring your parents
Terror looks like a fire, destroying your most prized possessions
Terror sounds like a bullet, whizzing past your head
Terror sounds like someone screaming, as they are murdered
Terror feels like a spider, crawling up your neck
Terror feels like a taunting presence, that you cannot see
Terror tastes like a bitter sweet, making you cough and splutter
Terror tastes like blood, pouring from a dead body
Terror reminds me of flying off my bike,
And scraping along the ground
Terror reminds me of a cricket ball, flying towards my head
Terror smells of an unwashed maniac,
While you hide in the cupboard
Terror smells of dried blood, as the police investigate a murder.

Mark McArthur (10)
Dean Park Primary School, Edinburgh

Wonder

Wonder feels like soft silk, in a barren land.
Wonder sounds like a gasp, from a person at their first sight
of a sunset above the sea.
Wonder sounds like the rush of air, when you are gliding in a plane.
Wonder is blue, like the sky on a sunny day.
Wonder is yellow, like the sun rising up in the morning.
Wonder reminds me of when I went to the Grand Canyon,
and saw how immense it is.
Wonder reminds me of when I saw a Fijian rugby player
run down the whole rugby pitch and score a try.
Wonder tastes like an amazing dish of food, cooked by
a terrible chef.
Wonder looks like a massive mountain on a snowy day.
Wonder smells like fresh air after a long day at the farmyard.

Murray Baxter (11)
Dean Park Primary School, Edinburgh

Surprise

Surprise feels like opening a big present on Christmas Day
and loving what it turns out to be.
Surprise reminds me of my 7th birthday
and seeing a big limo come to my house,
even though it wasn't the one I wanted.
I still had a great time but I would have liked a pink one.
Surprise is the colour of pinkie-red
when your face turns that colour
after being surprised by what you see.
Surprise smells like freshly baked chocolate chip cookies
taken out of the oven and left to cool down on the worktop.
Surprise looks like a very happy face with a massive smile.
Surprise sounds like lots of people cheering and clapping for you
if it's at a surprise birthday party or just in your head.
Surprise tastes like pink candyfloss melting in your mouth.

Amy Owens (10)
Dean Park Primary School, Edinburgh

Silence

Silence is yellow like the sun,
shining above the Earth making no sound.
Silence sounds like a calm blue sky,
towering above the children in the park.
Silence smells of a beautiful horse,
lonely in his stable, eating slowly.
Silence feels quiet and creepy,
in the woods on a dark night.
Silence looks like an explorer,
watching a new species of animal closely.
Silence reminds me of an empty house,
standing in the wilderness, standing on its last legs.
Silence tastes like water,
slowly going down my throat.

Lyn Ross (10)
Dean Park Primary School, Edinburgh

Sadness

Sadness sounds like a person being executed,
just like Mary Queen of Scots.
Sadness tastes like teardrops dripping down my face,
when I hurt myself.
Sadness smells of blood, if someone gets killed from your family.
Sadness reminds me of people that are in my family
who have died, that were very kind.
Sadness feels like I or you need care,
you need care, because you might get ill if you worry too much.
Sadness is black, because it is a sad time.
Sadness looks like a dark cloud in a sky,
it is a very sad time.

Hannah Ferguson (10)
Dean Park Primary School, Edinburgh

Love

Love tastes like some chocolate, that has been wrapped
in a lovely shiny box.
Love tastes like strawberries and whipped cream that is
in a bright red love bowl.
Love feels warm and cosy, on a hot summer's day.
Love's colour is red, like the very hot sun.
Love's colour is yellow, like the moon that shines at night.
Love reminds me of my family, when we are laughing together.
Love reminds me of my auntie's dog, when he licks my face.
Love looks like a big heart, that is full of love.
Love sounds like people saying they love each other, in romance.
Love smells like rosy perfume, that makes me think of love.

Kristi Divito (10)
Dean Park Primary School, Edinburgh

Fun

Fun reminds me of the water park slides around the world.
Fun reminds me of when I win a game of Pro Evolution Soccer 2009.
Fun is the colour of yellow because it is bright and full of joy.
Fun is the sound of people shouting and the running footsteps.
Fun is the sound of people laughing
and enjoying themselves in a park.
Fun looks like scoring a hat-trick in football.
Fun looks like bungee jumping in the sky as high as I can go.
Fun looks like opening your presents on a Christmas morning.
Fun smells like pizza made by Chicago Town.
Fun feels good because when you touch an animal it is
a cool feeling.

Nathan Collins (10)
Dean Park Primary School, Edinburgh

Silence

Silence is the colour of ice from some people's veins
Silence is the colour of black from outer space and beyond the stars
Silence is the colour of the clouds that never fade
Silence is the colour of water over the sea
Silence looks like a mannequin in a shop
Silence looks like a man born sideways over the moon
Silence looks like a clock that doesn't move
Silence reminds me of the icy cold winter days
Silence reminds me that there are no more children in the park
Silence reminds me of the two minute silence about the
men fighting in the war.

Kirsty Marriott (10)
Dean Park Primary School, Edinburgh

Surprise

Surprise sounds like children screaming out as loud as they can.
Surprise feels like a smooth leaf, like the wind in the air.
Surprise smells of melting chocolate on a marshmallow,
like a present that you always wanted.
Surprise reminds me of happy people enjoying themselves
more than ever before, the first man on the moon.
Surprise is the colour of blue, like clouds in the sky.
Surprise looks like birds in the sky twittering, like laying eggs.
Surprise sounds like people being happy all day long,
like having the best day ever.

Izaac Stenhouse (10)
Dean Park Primary School, Edinburgh

Courage

Courage tastes like water after a very trying show.
Courage reminds me of a leap or a jump in ballet
even if I hurt myself.
Courage feels like a hard and strong brick on a wall.
The colour that reminds me of courage is royal red
like the Queen's robe.
Courage looks like a lion, strong and brave.
Courage smells like make-up which I have to put on
before a ballet show.
Courage sounds like the music that beats on the floor.

Alexander Kennedy (10)
Dean Park Primary School, Edinburgh

Happiness

Happiness tastes like strawberries and cheese.
Happiness feels like a knitted coat from my granny.
Happiness reminds me of Dalkeith Country Park, with
the chocolate waffles.
Happiness sounds like the birds in the sky, singing me a song.
Happiness smells of chocolate, that's been melted.
Happiness is the colour of orange when the sun goes down.
Happiness looks like Christmas Day, all the kids
are opening presents.

Archie MacLean (10)
Dean Park Primary School, Edinburgh

Happiness

Happiness feels like playing with Lego,
Building a new power miner model.
Happiness is the colour of golden honey, on my toast in the morning.
Happiness sounds like music, on the radio.
Happiness reminds me of pancakes, with Nutella, rolled up.
Happiness tastes like Italian food, in my mouth.
Happiness looks like milk chocolate, in a cake before I eat it.
Happiness smells of pizza, made by Dominoes
And delivered to my door.

Cameron Taylor (10)
Dean Park Primary School, Edinburgh

Terror

Terror tastes like the tears of people crying at the funeral
of loved ones.
Terror's colour is black like a shadow lurking behind you.
Terror reminds me of having an asthma attack.
Terror feels like something inside you which is full of fear and scared.
Terror smells of blood.

Michael Bryce (10)
Dean Park Primary School, Edinburgh

Pain

Pain is dark and black, like thunder clouds.
Pain is dark red, like the blood when you cut yourself.
Pain reminds me of sadness, like when I hurt myself.
Pain tastes of tears, running down my face when I'm hurt.
Pain feels like a sore feeling in my tummy.
Pain sounds like someone screaming for help.
Pain smells like a hospital, going in for an operation.
Pain looks like someone with a broken leg that is swollen.

Ellie MacDowall (10)
Dean Park Primary School, Edinburgh

Joy

Joy is a colour of orange and yellow flowers in a field
Joy smells of my dog, when I play with her
Joy reminds me of my birthday party, when we dance
Joy looks like people laughing, people at a party having fun
Joy sounds like people at the seaside, people laughing
and playing in the sea
Joy feels warm and happy, like in my bed after a good day
Joy tastes like the chocolate, melting in your mouth.

Katie Bennett (10)
Dean Park Primary School, Edinburgh

Pain

Pain reminds you of when your dog dies, on your birthday.
Pain reminds you of when you fall out of a tree and break your leg.
Pain looks like a man lying in a pool of blood,
After he has been stabbed.
Pain looks like a man with an axe, savaging someone.
Pain looks like a gravestone, with flowers around it.
Pain sounds like someone screaming, after falling over.
Pain sounds like a splat after jumping off a cliff.

Joseph Mole (11)
Dean Park Primary School, Edinburgh

Anger

Anger looks like war, because people are shooting each other
Anger sounds like a gun being fired, because it makes a big bang
Anger smells of mushrooms, because I don't like them
Anger's colour is black and brown, because they are not bright
Anger feels like being annoyed, because someone has been mean
Anger tastes of roasted potatoes, because I don't like them
Anger reminds me of when my chicken died, because I really
liked my chicken.

Sybe Hoekstra (10)
Dean Park Primary School, Edinburgh

Sadness

Sadness tastes like water from the tap
Sadness sounds like tears dripping down your face, getting hurt
Sadness smells of salty water, my sister drinking it from the sea
Sadness' colour is navy blue, just like tears
Sadness looks like water stuck inside a crystal, trying to
get out and escape
Sadness reminds me of being at a funeral, remembering a friend
Sadness feels like a wave going up and down on a cold winter's day.

Alastair Lawrie (10)
Dean Park Primary School, Edinburgh

Fun

Fun is blue, like the deep blue ocean
Fun looks like a pool, full of water and fun
Fun feels like a balloon, static making your hair stick up
Fun is green, like rolling around in fresh grass
Fun looks like a cake, when you get your favourite birthday cake
Fun feels like a dolphin, too hard to explain how it feels
But no words can explain how overwhelmed with joy you are.

Rory Carrie (11)
Dean Park Primary School, Edinburgh

Happiness

Happiness feels like silky lavender, blowing in the wind.
Happiness is yellow like the sunset.
Happiness is the sound of children laughing in the park.
Happiness tastes like an ice cream on a hot summer's day.
Happiness smells like freshly cut grass.
Happiness reminds me of children having a snowball fight.
Happiness looks like lots of happy faces smiling and laughing.

Christopher Murdoch (10)
Dean Park Primary School, Edinburgh

Hallowe'en Poem

Moonlight wolves
Hats, rats and cats
Getting attacked
Moving, screaming
Teeth scratching
Try not to scream
It's Hallowe'en
It will give you a fright
Scary house
Bats flying everywhere
Beware, beware
Sticky sweets that witches use for spells
Don't scream
It's Hallowe'en.

Nicole Sutherland (9)
Kennoway Primary & Community School, Kennoway

Hallowe'en

Spooky spiders,
Glowing slime,
Vampires' fangs,
Witches' brooms,
Blood-curdling monster,
Powerful spells,
Phantoms' capes,
Haunted houses,
Howling wolves,
Witch's cauldron,
Ghost's moan,
Screaming people,
Howling owls.

Dylan Holmes (9)
Kennoway Primary & Community School, Kennoway

Cruel Ghouls

Cruel ghouls
Hiding in wool
A big ghost
That scares the most
A running mouse
In a haunted house
Witches' potions
Causing commotion
Vampires flying in the night
Giant spiders give you a fright
This is scary Hallowe'en
With many monsters horribly mean.

Rhys Menmuir (9)
Kennoway Primary & Community School, Kennoway

Hallowe'en

H allowe'en is scary
A lways very dark
L ight of the moon
L onely at night
O ther people hear howls
W itches on broomsticks
E ight hundred sweets
E verybody sees bloodshot eyes
N ever go out at night!

Ellie Forsyth (9)
Kennoway Primary & Community School, Kennoway

A Witch Always Dresses In Black

A witch always dresses in black.
She will have a scary cat.
Also a very pointy hat.
She can turn into a bat!

She mixes up her deadly potion.
Swirling, mixing, what a commotion.
It stinks, it smells, that horrible brew.
I'm glad I'm not in it, *phew!*

Gary Mitchell (9)
Kennoway Primary & Community School, Kennoway

Spider

S piders are freaky and give you a fright.
P ure black spiders crawl about at night.
I nvisible bugs attack you.
D eadly spiders can kill you.
E erie noises you can hear.
R are bugs come near here.

Rhys Gordon (9)
Kennoway Primary & Community School, Kennoway

Autumn

Autumn
Red squirrels collecting
Golden corn falling
Black birds flying
A gentle breeze blowing
Small twigs snapping
Orange leaves rustling
Autumn.

Jordan McCallum (8)
Kennoway Primary & Community School, Kennoway

Autumn

Autumn
Floppy scarecrow scaring
Hard conkers falling
Brown leaves dropping
Patterned kites flying
Little children playing
Bright sun shining
Autumn.

Olivia McGowan (8)
Kennoway Primary & Community School, Kennoway

Autumn

Autumn
Red leaves floating
Huge tractor ploughing
Busy farmer sowing
Brown leaves crunching
Blue kite flying
Strong wind blowing
Autumn.

Owen Thacker (8)
Kennoway Primary & Community School, Kennoway

Hallowe'en Poem

Pumpkin and potions
Vampires in motion
Ghosts and ghouls
Making all the rules
Spiders appearing everywhere
Trick or treat, if you dare
This is Hallowe'en
Try not to scream.

Dylan Sneddon (9)
Kennoway Primary & Community School, Kennoway

Autumn

Autumn
Green grass blowing
Bright sun shining
Bold conkers cracking
Red breast singing
Bronze leaves falling
Big pumpkins growing
Autumn.

Corrie Lironi (8)
Kennoway Primary & Community School, Kennoway

Autumn

Autumn
Multicoloured kites flying
Bright sun burning
Powerful wind blowing
Brown leaves falling
Giant tractors ploughing
Pretty birds flying
Autumn.

Robbie MacBride (8)
Kennoway Primary & Community School, Kennoway

Autumn

Autumn
Brown fir cones blowing
Large leaves floating
Countless farmers ploughing
Menacing scarecrow scaring
Strong wind blowing
Big sun shining
Autumn.

Codie Neill (8)
Kennoway Primary & Community School, Kennoway

Autumn

Autumn
Red bird singing
Brown leaves dropping
Yellow sun shining
Green conkers falling
Orange squirrels collecting
Golden pumpkins watching
Autumn.

Bryan Byers (8)
Kennoway Primary & Community School, Kennoway

Autumn

Autumn
Burgundy leaves swaying
Green combines cutting
Red squirrels gathering
Green conkers cracking
Big twigs snapping
Autumn.

Téa Jensen (7)
Kennoway Primary & Community School, Kennoway

Heart

H allowe'en
E cho in the dark
A cobweb in the haunted house
R oaring from devils
T ouch of poison!

Conor Gourlay (9)
Kennoway Primary & Community School, Kennoway

Mummy

M oaning and groaning
U p and out they crawl
M oving slowly towards you
M uttering evil thoughts
Y ou are *scared!*

Jozef Hill (9)
Kennoway Primary & Community School, Kennoway

Hallowe'en Poem

Witches and their cats.
Making potions with rats.
Big, black, hairy bats.
Witches sat down with their pointy hats.

Codie Doig (9)
Kennoway Primary & Community School, Kennoway

The Hallowe'en Poem

It was very, very dark one night,
Though something came out and gave me a fright,
It reminded me of costumes and sweets,
Then I saw a vampire trying to steal our treats,
Suddenly I saw a black witch go past,
And in fact she was going very fast,
There were lots of flashing lights to be seen,
A great variety of black and green,
I heard a lot of spooky sounds,
But it was only a few greyhounds,
I smelt a lot of yummy treats,
All the more for me to eat,
Zombies' faces were full of cuts,
I found them eating monkey nuts,
On Hallowe'en night ghosts like to scare,
So to all you children please beware!

Heather Johnstone (10)
Kirkstyle Primary School, Kilmarnock

Hallowe'en Poem

The colours of Hallowe'en are black, orange and red,
Tonight the wee children are not in their bed,
From witches to wizards and skeleton groups,
I can smell some people making pumpkin soup,
I can hear the wolves howling in the night,
I see two boys getting a fright,
I can still taste my tea in my mouth,
I see people in costumes running from house to house,
I look to see all my friends,
I see some girls that are making a den,
It appears like you're being followed,
By the people in the film called 'The Followers'
It reminds me of the film called 'Chucky'
Which is a film that is yucky.

Joe Murphy (10)
Kirkstyle Primary School, Kilmarnock

My Hallowe'en Poem

It's a Hallowe'en night and the streets are dark,
I am very scared when I go into the park,
I knock on someone's door and I smell sweets,
That's my favourite smell of treats,
I can hear the sound of screaming children,
But to witches it sounds like cats,
Witches also like the taste of rats,
I thought I had seen a ghost,
Turns out it was just a lamp post,
I felt tired walking around,
When I looked down I saw a pound,
It reminded me of a book I read,
When I was nicely tucked up in bed.

Cory Dunlop (10)
Kirkstyle Primary School, Kilmarnock

Hallowe'en

Ghosts, freaks, goblins and ghouls,
A wee bit like our teachers at school,
When it's dark we all go out scaring,
Frightening neighbours with the costumes we're wearing.
'Trick or treat?' that's what we say,
And do a wee jig, a joke or a play.
Toffee apples I was given,
One big bite and you're in toffee heaven,
Happy Hallowe'en is what it's about,
To scare as many people as we run, scream and shout.

Baillie Fawns Robertson (10)
Kirkstyle Primary School, Kilmarnock

Hallowe'en

Ghosts, freaks, goblins and ghouls,
Are a little bit like our teachers at school,
They shout and scream and make a noise,
But not as much as scary boys,
The thought of treats behind closed doors
Will make us knock and let out roars,
The pumpkin lantern smiles and flickers,
With any luck I'll get some Snickers,
With bags full, it's home through the park,
And leave the ghosts and ghouls in the dark!

Chloe Bole (10)
Kirkstyle Primary School, Kilmarnock

Hallowe'en

Hallowe'en has finally come,
Let's all go and have some fun,
Yummy sweets and pretty treats,
Gives us all lots to eat,
With toffee apples and chocolate too,
Also ghosts that go, *'Boo!'*
Red devils and candles bright,
Orange pumpkins that light up the night,
Hallowe'en has been and passed,
And we all had a blast.

Jessica McCrum (10)
Kirkstyle Primary School, Kilmarnock

Hallowe'en

I walk round the streets under the dark black sky,
As people with costumes slowly stroll by,
I smell lots of candy and other sweets,
There will be lots of scares as well as treats,
I see scary costumes from the corner of my eye,
And I feel like there's spirits and ghosts flying by,
I hear ghosts wailing and skeletons clunking,
I'm off to the tub for some apple dunking,
I'm scared and filled with lots of fear,
But I'll be back for my Hallowe'en next year!

Zoe Horner (10)
Kirkstyle Primary School, Kilmarnock

Hallowe'en Night

It's Hallowe'en night,
And the colours are bright,
The sound of a wolf's cry,
Fills the sky,
Kids get dressed up like goblins and ghouls,
And some dressed like proper fools,
Dark spirits roam the streets,
And children run around shouting, 'Trick or treat?'
On Hallowe'en night do be aware,
For something might just give you a scare.

Ty O'Donnell (9)
Kirkstyle Primary School, Kilmarnock

Hallowe'en Poem

A witch dressed in black,
Went out in the dark,
She rode on her broom,
And went for a zoom,
Her cat held on tight,
As he was afraid of the height,
And the owl said, 'Hoot!'
When the witch lost her boot,
It hit a frog,
Who was in the bog.

Callum Gibson (10)
Kirkstyle Primary School, Kilmarnock

Hallowe'en Night

In the blackness of Hallowe'en night,
Dark shadows will appear,
Scary witches, skeletons and ghouls,
Will have everyone shaking with fear,
An orange pumpkin in my hand,
I'm dressing up as a girl from a band,
Trick or treating with my friend,
I wish this night would never end,
Collecting chocolates, apples and delicious sweets,
And lots and lots of other treats.

Kim Law (10)
Kirkstyle Primary School, Kilmarnock

Happiness

Happiness is a bright rainbow colour like soft ribbon
on a wrapped present.
It smells of sweet smelling roses among freshly cut grass,
And sounds like calm, soothing waves overlapping each other
on the sea.
Happiness tastes like sweet, twinkling sugar as it pops
on my tongue.
It looks like soft, icy snowflakes on dark green trees that sparkle,
And feels like small, squishy marshmallows on top of warm
hot chocolate.
Happiness lives in my heart forever.
Happiness reminds me of a bright yellow sun looking down
on a calm, sandy beach.

Rebecca Wilson (11)
Lenzie Moss Primary School, Lenzie

Happiness

Happiness is the colour of bright fluorescent lights
shining down upon the dance floor.
It smells of freshly cut grass as I roll quickly down the hill,
and sounds like birds singing in trees on a summer's day.
Happiness tastes like Ben and Jerry's Caramel Chew Chew
ice cream as it melts in my mouth.
It looks like a newborn kitten playing with a ball of string,
and feels like a cockapoo puppy as I hold it in my arms.
Happiness lives among us as we play and laugh.
Happiness reminds me of pulling the first present from
the Christmas tree.

Robyn Magowan (11)
Lenzie Moss Primary School, Lenzie

Happiness

Happiness is as green as newly grown grass.
It smells of new made chocolate melting under the heat,
And it sounds like laughter from kids playing around on the bright blue seesaw in the park.
Happiness tastes like ice cream with sprinkles
on a hot summer's day.
Happiness looks like a cute puppy playing with a ball
in the back garden,
And it feels like playing on the beach on a sunny day.
Happiness reminds me of Christmas Day
When I am opening my presents.

Alex Magowan (11)
Lenzie Moss Primary School, Lenzie

Happiness

Happiness is the colour of a firework exploding in the night sky.
It smells of pizza freshly baked from Italy,
And sounds like a hummingbird singing from the tree.
Happiness tastes like chocolate melting sweetly in my mouth.
It looks like an Xbox on the Game store's shelf,
And feels like a gentle pillow on the end of my bed waiting to soothe me to sleep.
Happiness lives inside of us, waiting to burst out.
Happiness reminds me of Christmas morning when joy is spreading through the air.

Ben Waddell (11)
Lenzie Moss Primary School, Lenzie

Terror

Terror is dark like the night sky
Terror smells horrible and vile,
Like the stench of the underground sewers.
It sounds like people's screaming voices during the night.
Terror tastes like the blood from innocent corpses.
Terror looks like bodies used as sandbags
to protect the men and women who fight for freedom.
It feels like anger, fear and pain.
It lives in every trespasser, murder and sinner.
Terror reminds people of terrible wars and horrific memories.

Aaron Hannah (11)
Lenzie Moss Primary School, Lenzie

Dreams

Dreams are the colour of big fluffy white clouds shaped like
rabbits and ducks.
They smell of honey and syrup melting on the tip of my tongue,
and sound like angels playing harps on the gates of Heaven.
Dreams taste like a river of pure and fresh water.
They look like the wet dew on freshly cut grass or on a spider's web
with the sun setting behind the hill far in the horizon,
and feels like a never-ending pit of soft and melting goo.
Dreams live in your mind waiting to be explored and shared.
Dreams remind me of happiness and my friends.

Ryan John Davidson (11)
Lenzie Moss Primary School, Lenzie

Exhilaration

Exhilaration is the lightest colour imaginable, painted
On the walls of victory.
Exhilaration smells like a rose bush blossoming in spring.
Exhilaration sounds like laughter which never stops.
Exhilaration tastes of the freshest apples
In the most beautiful orchard.
Exhilaration looks like a sunny day on a beach.
Exhilaration feels sleek and smooth, like the finest silk.
Exhilaration lives in the hearts and minds of people.
Exhilaration reminds me of the people I know.

Euan Doig (11)
Lenzie Moss Primary School, Lenzie

Fear

Fear is the colour black, it blinds you even in the light.
It smells of dampness, it's wet and sad
And sounds like thunder rolling through the dark, gloomy sky.
Fear tastes like a dried up piece of bread, stale and scratchy.
It looks like a stormy night out at sea, the waves crashing
big and strong, even taller than me.
And feels like you're choking, gasping for air. It makes you feel cold.
Fear lives in a dark cave far away, but at the same time,
much closer than you think.
Fear reminds me of a dark corner, untouched and empty.

Beth Whitelaw (11)
Lenzie Moss Primary School, Lenzie

Hatred

Hatred is boiling, seething, bright, burning red.
It smells of putrid rotten eggs on a hot day,
And sounds like a broken, cracked tune of sorrow.
Hatred tastes like a platter of spoiled food.
It looks like a disgusting creature running through the streets,
And feels like you are being torn and emptied of all happiness and hope.
Hatred lives near happy children ready to spoil their day.
Hatred reminds me of despairing people crying for friends they haven't got.

Liam Tierney (11)
Lenzie Moss Primary School, Lenzie

Relief

Relief is the colour of the sunset, like the end of the day.
It smells of roses growing in the golden fields
Which the sun shines bright on.
It sounds of laughter and people having a good time.
It tastes of Galaxy chocolate melting on the tip of my tongue.
It looks like happy faces smiling at each other.
It feels like soft silky sponges waiting to be laid on.
It lives in the heart within you.
It reminds me of my mum and dad.

Euan McBride (10)
Lenzie Moss Primary School, Lenzie

Love

Love is bright red, like petals on a rose.
It smells like fresh daisies plucked with clean hands
And sounds like music, romantically playing in a restaurant.
Love tastes like lips pressing together, softly in the distance.
It looks heart-warming and shiny, like a wedding ring.
And feels soft and feather-like when it swishes through your body.
Love lives in my heart and passes through to that special person
And from there it will never move.
It reminds me of the time I kissed his lips.

Shauna Adair (10)
Lenzie Moss Primary School, Lenzie

Surprise

Surprise is gold like a medal from the Olympics,
It smells of chocolate from Cadbury's chocolate factory,
And sounds like rock music coming from a CD player,
Surprise tastes like a toffee apple,
It looks like balloons and banners with 'Surprise!' on them,
And feels like cream in the middle of a meringue,
Surprise lives in the future,
Surprise reminds me of my cousin's birthday party
Earlier in the year.

Douglas Bennie (11)
Lenzie Moss Primary School, Lenzie

Courage

Courage feels like pride running through my veins.
It smells of sweets and candy and looks like happy faces.
Courage is gold, shiny, twinkly and precious.
It sounds of laughter in a funfair and tastes of jelly beans.
Courage lives on the treetops, swaying in the wind.
Courage reminds me of my dad, so brave yet so happy.

Amy MacLeod (10)
Lenzie Moss Primary School, Lenzie

Jealousy

Jealousy is red, like wobbly jelly.
It smells sour and bitter, like rotting food.
It sounds like a chimney puffing over and over again.
It tastes like hot chilli.
Jealousy looks mean and angry like a bully.
It feels irritating like a mum embarrassing you.
It lives in your mind, trapped, trying to get out.
Jealousy reminds you of something you want to forget
But keeps coming back to you.

Laura Bamford (9)
Lenzie Moss Primary School, Lenzie

Happiness

Happiness is orange as when the sun rises.
It smells like flowers just harvested from the field,
And sounds like the ocean tide coming in.
Happiness tastes like sweet caramel chocolate.
It looks like the moon staring down at a lot of countries,
And feels like the wind hitting off my hot cheeks when
I am on my bike.
Happiness reminds me of the nice hot Christmas dinner
covered in delicious gravy.

Gary Robertson (11)
Lenzie Moss Primary School, Lenzie

Pride

Pride is golden coloured, 24 carat that is.
It smells of richness, like the Queen's palace.
And sounds like hundreds and thousands of people
Cheering your name.
Pride tastes of a Thorntons chocolate fountain and looks like respect.
Pride reminds me of starting P1 in my shirt and tic.

Fraser Bissett (11)
Lenzie Moss Primary School, Lenzie

Fear

Fear is as dark as the night sky and you can't see a thing
Fear smells nothing, nothing you can ever imagine
Fear sounds like screams from a thousand corpses
Fear tastes like eyeballs in a soup bowl of blood
Fear looks like a ghost with one eye, sixteen tentacles and no soul
Fear feels like a sword piercing your skin
And searing through your heart
Fear lives beside your heart, fighting its way to take over your body
Fear reminds you of a nightmare you'll wish you'd never had.

Innes Guthrie Mackay (11)
Lenzie Moss Primary School, Lenzie

Sadness

Sadness is a dark blue gloomy colour on a rainy morning.
It smells like a fiery, burning smell coming from the toaster
when toast is burnt.
And sounds like loud frightful screaming from people fighting.
It tastes like liquorice sticking between my teeth.
It looks like a cloud ready to burst with rain,
And feels like crunchy rocks under my feet.
Sadness lives in thundery sky forever.
Sadness reminds me of sitting in a corner with no one to talk to.

Caitlyn Harris (10)
Lenzie Moss Primary School, Lenzie

Terror

Terror looks like a pale white face
Terror smells like burnt toast
Terror sounds like screaming
Terror tastes like sour milk
Terror looks like children running in fear
Terror lives in everyone at one point
Terror feels like mould
Terror reminds me of my loft.

Andrew Crawford (10)
Lenzie Moss Primary School, Lenzie

Fear

Fear is as dark as night
And smells of smoke from a fire.
Fear sounds like screams from nowhere
And it tastes like raw chicken with cold blood on top.
Fear looks like a pitch-black graveyard
And feels like hard stone.
It lives in a cave in the middle of nowhere.
Fear reminds me of anger and ghosts.

Ashleigh Harris (11)
Lenzie Moss Primary School, Lenzie

Terror

Terror is the colour of a tornado wreaking havoc in a town.
It smells like dustbins blowing in the wind.
It sounds like a fox howling in the night.
Terror tastes metallic, just sitting in your mouth.
It looks like burglars robbing a home.
It feels like nails in your hand.
It lives in a bad part of you.
Terror reminds me of rage and jealousy in your mind.

Cameron Mack (10)
Lenzie Moss Primary School, Lenzie

Jealousy

Jealousy is the colour black
It smells like a clammy old room
It sounds like laughter but not involving me
Jealousy tastes like sour lemons
It looks like darkness and a bright light far away
It feels like an ice cube melting in my hand
Jealousy lives inside of you, inside of everyone
It reminds me of when they were nice and unrich.

Arran McCahill (11)
Lenzie Moss Primary School, Lenzie

Anger

Anger is blood-red like fire burning through the wood.
It smells like thick black smoke burning in the fire,
And sounds like a raging bull charging over a field.
Anger tastes like a cup full of ginger beer in my mouth.
It looks like my brother having a temper when he doesn't
get his own way.
Anger feels like agonising pain when you fall and skin your knee.
Anger reminds me of how bad my temper can be!

Christopher Findlay (11)
Lenzie Moss Primary School, Lenzie

Happiness

Happiness is luminous colours in the rainbow.
It smells of pineapple on a tropical island,
And sounds like birds chirping in the morning.
Happiness tastes like chocolate fudge cake smothered
in caramel and toffee.
It looks like a bunch of flowers from the garden,
And feels like bunnies in the field.
Happiness reminds me of my family and friends.

Jack Morrison (11)
Lenzie Moss Primary School, Lenzie

Love

Love is the colour of scarlet red flowing through my veins.
It smells of roses, the scent blowing through the wind,
And sounds like music, a love song written just for me.
Love tastes like ripe strawberries and cream with sugar on top.
It looks like bright stars sparkling in the night sky,
And feels like satin sheets against your skin.
Love lives in the heart, beating like a drum.
Love reminds me of the sun setting against the sea.

Lauren Jones (11)
Lenzie Moss Primary School, Lenzie

Dreamy

Dreamy is floating to the clouds up high.
It smells like the fresh air in the sky
And sounds like people as they meet.
Dreamy tastes like a sugary sweet.
It looks like a puppy chasing its tail
And feels like the wind as the boat sets sail.
Dreamy lives inside our heads.
Dreamy reminds me of my cosy bed.

Karen Millin (11)
Lenzie Moss Primary School, Lenzie

Courage

Courage is blue, like the clouds and sky
It smells like oranges, fresh from the orchard
And it sounds like confidence from your own beating heart
Courage tastes like fresh strawberries from a strawberry patch
It looks like lemon, from the pile of sour lemons
And feels like something new is going to happen
Courage lives in your heart
Courage reminds me of my confidence!

Rebecca Cheryl Lesurf (10)
Lenzie Moss Primary School, Lenzie

Joy

Joy is as yellow as the sun on a bright sunny day.
It smells like freshly cut grass sending out its scent
to the sunny summer sun.
And sounds like a sweet melody entering my ears.
Joy tastes like chocolate chip cookies that melt in my mouth.
It looks like a freshly opened daffodil bud on the first day of spring
And feels like a soft white feather fallen from a dove.
Joy reminds me of hot chocolate with marshmallows slowly melting.

Ewan Sydserff (10)
Lenzie Moss Primary School, Lenzie

Happiness

Happiness is a blue sea, calm and peaceful.
It smells like the seaweed that is gently floating on the surface,
And the sound of the waves crashing makes me relax.
I can taste the salt on the tip of my tongue.
It looks like a home for the dolphins and fishes.
I love the feeling of the water lapping around my neck.
It reminds me of lying on my rubber ring.

Laura Chalmers (10)
Lenzie Moss Primary School, Lenzie

Happiness

Happiness is red in the sky in the morning.
It smells like flowers on the window sill,
And sounds like music in the wartime.
Happiness tastes like food in the poor people's pans.
It looks like a football on the playground,
And feels like teddy bears on children's beds.
It reminds me of today - the day that war broke out.

Hongbo Guo (11)
Lenzie Moss Primary School, Lenzie

Sadness

Sadness is as grey as clouds on a miserable day.
It smells of burning wood on a cold day,
and sounds like people crying after someone has left them.
Sadness tastes like burnt toast in the morning.
It looks like a puppy with no owner on a cold misty day.
It feels like being in a room where you are not wanted.
Sadness reminds me of when my hamster died.

Rachael Smith (11)
Lenzie Moss Primary School, Lenzie

Fear

Fear is dull grey, like a tornado.
It smells of gas like my dad's car
And sounds like screaming like a tortured ghost.
It tastes like poison, just like drugs
And feels like fire burning, like barbecues.
It lives in Hell, like the Devil
And reminds me of parents' night.

Alasdair Jamieson (10)
Lenzie Moss Primary School, Lenzie

Pride

Pride is green like cut grass.
Pride smells like chocolate, like a Magnum.
Pride feels like you're happy but you're sad.
Pride reminds me of people singing in a choir.
Pride tastes of ice cream freezing in my mouth.
Pride lives in the air but you cannot see it.
Pride looks like people playing football.

Jack Savage (11)
Lenzie Moss Primary School, Lenzie

Anger

Anger is black and blue like a bruised sky.
It smells like the Amazon forest
And it sounds like the ear-splitting screams from baby foxes.
Anger tastes like a red hot chilli burning a hole through your tongue.
It looks like a single fire roasting through a wood
And feels like the back of a prehistoric dinosaur.
It reminds me of a wet, wild and windy morning.

Holly Anderson (11)
Lenzie Moss Primary School, Lenzie

Little Leaf

A jaggy pointy leaf
Sailing down like
A plane drifting in the air.

A colourful leaf
Swooping down
Like an eagle
With eyes on its prey.

A jaggy leaf
Diving down
Like a whale
Just out of water.

A crispy leaf
Gliding down
Like a kite.

A smooth leaf
Swimming down
Like a fish.

Andrew Timmins (10)
Oxgangs Primary School, Edinburgh

Autumn Is Coming

A swaying leaf
Goes tumbling down
Like a wave

A spiky leaf
Falling down
Like a tree falling

A soft leaf
Swishing down
Like wind swaying

A weird leaf
Floating down
Like a bird

A curvy leaf
Swooping down
Like a boat on water

An old leaf
Rushing down
Like a person in a rush

A new leaf
Sweeping down
Like a broom.

Cheney McQuillin (10)
Oxgangs Primary School, Edinburgh

Autumn Poem

A shiny bright green leaf
Swishes down
Like a big golden eagle.

A crispy fragile leaf
Is dropping down
Like a bottle dropping down on the ground.

A baby blue leaf
Swirls lightly down
Like a feather.

A crumbly leaf
Glides down
Like a paper aeroplane.

A jaggy leaf
Flutters down
Like a crisp packet in a bin.

Amy Harvey (10)
Oxgangs Primary School, Edinburgh

A Little Long Leaf

A crispy, brown leaf
Diving fast through the air
Like an aeroplane landing.

A slender leaf
Swooping down from the sky
Like an F1 car.

A jaggy leaf
Swimming down
Through the wet, rainy air.

A velvety, soft leaf
Gliding down
Like a falcon.

James Cornwall (10)
Oxgangs Primary School, Edinburgh

Autumn Poem

A soft leaf
Glides down
Like a golden eagle.

A damaged leaf
Swoops down
Like a scary black bat.

A colourful leaf
Flutters down
Like a delicate butterfly.

Gliding
Swooping
Fluttering
To the colourful autumn ground.

Demi Cumming (10)
Oxgangs Primary School, Edinburgh

An Awesomely Amazing Leaf

A slender leaf
Floating down
Like a velvet scarf flying around.

A small brown leaf
Soaring down
Like a little robin singing with no frown.

A silky leaf
Running down
Like a marathon runner wearing a crown.

Yusra Qureshi (9)
Oxgangs Primary School, Edinburgh

Autumn Poetry Writing

A crispy leaf
Gliding down
Like a bird of prey.

A soggy leaf
Dives down
Like a diver.

A smooth leaf
Sails down
Like a boat.

Bradley Wood (9)
Oxgangs Primary School, Edinburgh

Autumn Poetry Writing

A colourful leaf
Swooping down
Like a twirling tornado.

A slender leaf
Dropping down
Like a floating bird.

A gliding leaf
Floats down
Like a silk parachute.

Jack Purvis (10)
Oxgangs Primary School, Edinburgh

An Autumn Leaf

A fragile leaf
Floats down
Like a little butterfly flying away.

A graceful leaf
Falls down
Like a little ballet dancer.

A soft leaf
Flutters down
Like a delicate butterfly.

Megan Cowper (10)
Oxgangs Primary School, Edinburgh

An Autumn Leaf

A pointy leaf
Comes swooping down
Like a dangerous golden eagle.

A smooth leaf
Flutters down
Like a tiny dancer.

A colourful leaf
Came gliding down
Like a very fast bird.

Rachael Hannah Black (9)
Oxgangs Primary School, Edinburgh

An Autumnal Leaf

A smooth leaf
Sailing down
Like a yacht on the open sea.

A crispy leaf
Glides down
Like an aeroplane gliding down.

A fragile leaf
Flutters down
Like a beautiful butterfly flying away.

Abigail Burrows (10)
Oxgangs Primary School, Edinburgh

Autumn Poem

A crispy leaf
Floating down
Like a wave.

A crumbly leaf
Diving down
Like an amazing diver.

A soggy leaf
Gliding down
Like a golf ball.

Aiden Longrigg (9)
Oxgangs Primary School, Edinburgh

An Autumnal Leaf Poem

A colourful leaf
Flutters down
Like a butterfly coming down for landing

A crispy leaf
Swoops down
Like a golden eagle getting its prey

A pointy leaf
Tumbled down
Like an acrobat on the trapeze.

Amy Murphy (10)
Oxgangs Primary School, Edinburgh

I Can't Write A Poem

(Based on 'I Can't Write A Poem' by Bruce Lansky)

I have a French lesson to go to!
What's the point?
I don't know what a poem is!
What's my name?
I have homework to do!
My pen is leaking!
I have to do the weekly shopping!
I'm at the wrong school!
My arms have just turned into jelly!
I don't know how to!
My words are mush!
Bring! Bring! The bell just went!
It's two in the morning!
My glasses broke!
Time's up? Uh oh!
All I have is this dumb list of excuses.
You like it? Really?
I should have known,
I'm always the best at everything!

Millie Anderson (10)
Riverside Primary School, Stirling

Poem Triumph

Triumph the colour,
Gold,
And very bold,
Triumph the colour.

Triumph the smell,
All that's great,
On a plate,
Triumph the smell.

Triumph the sound,
Humans shouting
And bawling,
Triumph the sound.

Triumph the taste,
Lovely gold metal,
For a medal,
Triumph the taste.

What triumph looks like,
Humans celebrating,
And I'm not bluffing,
What triumph looks like.

What triumph feels like,
Victory,
Not glory,
What triumph feels like.

What triumph reminds me of,
Why I was born,
And why I eat corn,
What triumph reminds me of.

Ruairidh Swan (11)
Riverside Primary School, Stirling

I Can't Write A Poem

(Based on 'I Can't Write A Poem' by Bruce Lansky)

A poem! Not me!
I don't have a pencil.
My mum cooked my jotter instead of the chicken.
I'm allergic to work.
My dog ate my jotter.
I feel sick.
Too tired.
I've no lead in my pencil.
My pencil snapped.
I can't write.
My brain disappeared.
My fish ate my pencil.
I'm too hot.
My hands are too big.
I've broken my finger.
I've lost my pencil.
I've no pages in my jotter.
It's illegal to write poems
Don't you read the papers?
And besides poems are for adults.

Time's up? Uh oh!
Uh oh! All I have is this dumb list of excuses.
You like it? Really?
Thanks a lot.
I knew I could do it!

Ruth Allison (9)
Riverside Primary School, Stirling

I Can't Write A Poem

(Based on 'I Can't Write A Poem' by Bruce Lansky)

Huh?
Me writing a poem!
No, seriously.
Anyway my brain ran away.
My jotter flew out the window.
Plus my brain's smaller than a peanut.
I'm going to be sick.
My mum told me writing poems is illegal.
But I don't know how to write.
Anyway I don't know what a poem is!
I am allergic to work.
I don't want to.
My poetry skills are *rubbish!*
I am *bursting* for the toilet.
I've got better things to do.
I'm tied to my chair.
What is this - a joke?

Time's up? Uh oh!
All I have is this dumb list of excuses.
You like it? Really?
Thanks a lot.
I'm the best poet ever,
Better than Robbie Burns!

Flynn Starrs (9)
Riverside Primary School, Stirling

Leaves

Autumn leaves
Gold and brown
Dancing and curling to the ground
Dancing from morning till night
Until you see the lamp post light up.

Gabby Davidson (8)
Riverside Primary School, Stirling

Sadness

Black and gloomy,
Sadness is sharp,
It tastes so sour,
It feels heavy and dark,
Sadness is like a horrible misty day.

Sadness is hard,
It pulls you down,
It brings tears to your eye,
It pulls you back tough and sore,
It smells of burning and makes you want to cry.

Thundering, booming noises,
Fill the air,
You feel lonely,
The despair and anger,
Gets to you desperately.

Sadness hurts like lightning,
Striking during winter,
Cold and windy,
Wet and stormy,
Sadness is loud and hurts your ears,
Sadness is dark like the night,
Closing on you with no light.

Anna Reilly (9)
Riverside Primary School, Stirling

Leaves

Autumn leaves fall from the trees
And filter down to the cold ground.
Gold leaves, it means it's autumn time,
Lots of leaves are on the ground.
Boys and girls collect lots of conkers
And play games by rolling them.

Ryan Morrison (7)
Riverside Primary School, Stirling

Hope

Hope is yellow,
It smells of lilies, lovely to see,
Still sprouting desperately
And trying to get free.

Hope tastes of scones,
From the oven still warm,
With fresh jam and cream
Strawberries and all.

Hope sounds like a storm fading
Clouds clearing from the sky,
Hope is an unexpected wish,
To share with you and I.

Hope feels alive and strong,
Like a red rose growing,
Hope feels joyful and happy,
Like the sun blazing and glowing.

Hope looks like a gleeful family,
Playing on the beach,
Hope washes away the sadness,
Like dirt drained from a sheet with bleach.

Bethany MacKay (10)
Riverside Primary School, Stirling

Fear

Fear is black like shadows in Hell and black water.
Fear sounds like screams from ghosts and spooks
from scary places below.
Fear smells like sweat and tears.
Fear feels like shivers coming down your back and butterflies
in your stomach.
Fear looks like darkness all around with a single red light flickering.
Fear is a reminder of death.

Stuart MacGregor (11)
Riverside Primary School, Stirling

I Can't Write A Poem

(Based on 'I Can't Write A Poem' by Bruce Lansky)

I can't write
I'm blind and deaf
I hurt my head
I have brain damage
I can't be bothered to
My mobile is on speaker
I'm on the mobile to the President
I'm watching the Rangers game
Staring at my girlfriend
Watching the X Factor
I'm too hot
I'm invisible
I'm too strong, I'll break the pencil
The fire alarm went off
My hair is on fire
I'm going to sleep
Time's up? Uh oh!
All I have is this dumb list of excuses
You like it? Really?
I knew I was the best!

Ruairidh Cunningham (10)
Riverside Primary School, Stirling

Leaves

Autumn leaves
of gold and brown
see them swaying
to the ground
what a sight to see
such fun to see
as they dance to the ground
what fun to see the leaves
in autumn.

Gemma Watmore (8)
Riverside Primary School, Stirling

I Can't Write A Poem

(Based on 'I Can't Write A Poem' by Bruce Lansky)

No way, Jose!
I'm never in a million years writing a poem!
It's too late.
I'm tired.
The cat's eaten my jotter!
And the dog's eaten the cat!
And the hamster's strangely eaten the dog!
Besides, I never had a pencil in the first place.
Poems are for geeks
And actually I've just blown up my brain.
In fact, my mum went blind
And ate my rubber instead of the chicken.
And by the way, I need the toilet Miss.

Time's up? Uh oh!
All I have is this dumb list of excuses.
You like it? Really?
Thanks a lot.
I always thought I was great at doing poems.

Angus MacDougall (9)
Riverside Primary School, Stirling

I Can't Write A Poem

(Based on 'I Can't Write A Poem' by Bruce Lansky)

I woke up at two o'clock and my hamster had eaten my pencil.
Are you joking - me write a poem?
My jotter has no space left in it.
I have a sore hand and I can't write anything.
I have a sore tummy - I think I'll be sick!
Time's up, uh oh!
All I have is this dumb list of excuses.
You like it?
Really?
Thanks a lot.

Karol Hudak (8)
Riverside Primary School, Stirling

I Can't Write A Poem
(Based on 'I Can't Write A Poem' by Bruce Lansky)

A poem!

There has got to be a mistake
And besides my pencil is bendy
I feel sick
My mum said I am to go home at half past three
I need the toilet
My finger is jammed
I am dizzy
I have a cold
I am allergic to wood and paper
I am too hungry
I am an alien
My mind is lost
Time's up? Uh oh!
All I have is this dumb list of excuses
You like it? Really?
Thanks a lot.
I am great and I am relieved!

Katie Mackenie (9)
Riverside Primary School, Stirling

I Can't Write A Poem
(Based on 'I Can't Write A Poem' by Bruce Lansky)

You've got to be joking me!
My brother was so angry he broke all my pencils.
The bus ran over my glasses.
A dog peed on my jotter!
I was in such a rush, I dropped all my pencils.
Time's up? Uh oh!
All I have is this dumb list of excuses.
You like it? Really?
Thanks a lot!
I knew if I tried I could do it.

Megan Léonard (9)
Riverside Primary School, Stirling

I Can't Write A Poem
(Based on 'I Can't Write A Poem' by Bruce Lansky)

No! No! No! No! *No!*
Do I have to do this torture?
I'm dizzy, I'm allergic to paper, wood and pencils.
I jammed my finger in the door.
I don't know what to do!
My dog bit my hand off!
I need the toilet, I'm thirsty!
I need to do it on the computer.
The desk is too small.
I need a calculator.
I don't have a pencil.
I have a headache.

Time's up, uh oh!
All I have is this dumb list of excuses.
You like it?
Really?
Thanks a lot.

Rory Duncan (9)
Riverside Primary School, Stirling

I Can't Write A Poem
(Based on 'I Can't Write A Poem' by Bruce Lansky)

I can't write a poem.
Me? You must be joking!
My hamster has eaten my brain.
I've lost my thinking cap.
The dog's eaten my jotter.
Argh! An invisible yeti is coming to get me.
I'm allergic to my jotter at school.
Time's up? Uh oh!
All I have is this dumb list of excuses.
You like it? Really?
Thanks a lot, I'm great at writing poems!

Morgan MacLeod (9)
Riverside Primary School, Stirling

I Can't Write A Poem
(Based on 'I Can't Write A Poem' by Bruce Lansky)

Oh no,
It's poem time again!
I really need the loo!
And a crocodile stole my ideas!
It's far too noisy.
I come from Mars!
I haven't a clue what the teacher's on about!
A dog bit my jotter.
My hand is sore, I am bored to tears.
I don't feel well.
I didn't go to sleep last night.
I have a headache.
It's too late in the day.

Time's up? Uh oh!
All I have is this dumb list of excuses.
You like it? Really?
Thanks a lot.

Charley-Marie Wilson (8)
Riverside Primary School, Stirling

I Can't Write A Poem
(Based on 'I Can't Write A Poem' by Bruce Lansky)

What? A poem, you are kidding me!
Do you think I am a genius?
My brain is fried!
Aliens abducted my pencil and jotter!
I have got to go to the doctors!
Time's up? Uh oh!
All I have is this dumb list of excuses.
You like it?
Really?
Thanks a lot.
I knew I was the best!

Molly Mack (8)
Riverside Primary School, Stirling

I Can't Write A Poem

(Based on 'I Can't Write A Poem' by Bruce Lansky)

No way
No I can't
Besides my dog ate my pencil case
The pencil got abducted by aliens
My jotter's fallen down the toilet
My fish ate my pencil
My cat ate my fish, my dog ate my cat
We took the dog to Australia and it got eaten by a shark
And then no one volunteered to go down and kill the shark
So I'm pencil-less
And poems are for girls
And did I mention that my brain exploded?
Time's up? Uh oh!
All I have is this dumb list of excuses.
You like it, really?
Thanks a lot.
I didn't know I could write a poem, yay me!

Matthew Dawson (9)
Riverside Primary School, Stirling

Sadness

Sadness is tears falling from your face,
Sadness is worries,
Worries that are stuck in your head and can't get out.

You can be sad when you are lonely,
Black clouds filling in the sky.

Crime,
People getting murdered,
Sadness is dying, crying, screaming and most of all,
Breaking up of friends because at the end there is no more.

Sadness,
Is one feeling that you don't want.

Sean McGrandles (10)
Riverside Primary School, Stirling

I Can't Write A Poem
(Based on 'I Can't Write A Poem' by Bruce Lansky)

No way!
Not me!
I can't write a poem!
My paper got flushed down the toilet.
I've gone blind!
I'm allergic to poems.
I'm bursting for the loo.
I scribbled on my paper with pen.
I left my pencil at home and my dog ate it!
And my mum cooked my spare ones.
There's a wasp in the classroom.
My hands are broken!
Time's up? Uh oh!
All I have is a dumb list of excuses.
You like it? Really?
Thanks a lot.
I'm not as bad as I thought at poems.

Jasmine Hunter (10)
Riverside Primary School, Stirling

I Can't Write A Poem
(Based on 'I Can't Write A Poem' by Bruce Lansky)

What a poem!
You must be kidding me!
I've lost my rubber and my pencil!
I need the toilet!
I lost my glasses on the bus!
My hamster nibbled my jotter!
Time's up? Uh oh!
All I have is this dumb list of excuses.
You like it? Really?
Thanks a lot.
I am the best writer in P5M.

Molly McCarry (8)
Riverside Primary School, Stirling

I Can't Write A Poem

(Based on 'I Can't Write A Poem' by Bruce Lansky)

You must be joking
My pencil is broken
I don't have a sharpener
And someone has stolen my other pencil
I have broken my arm
But I need the toilet
Oh my gosh - someone is stealing my bike
And I will have to run downstairs
I need to go to the dentist now
I forgot to have my lunch
Now I feel sick
I'm also tired!
Time's up? Uh oh!
All I have done is this dumb list of excuses
You like it? Really?
I never knew I could write a poem.
My poem *rocks!*

Lewis Ralston (9)
Riverside Primary School, Stirling

Autumn Leaves

Leaves
Are now
Drifting
Slowly
Down.
When you touch them
They may break.
They tumble
When the wind blows.
What lovely things
Leaves do.

Emma Dawson (7)
Riverside Primary School, Stirling

Love

The colour of love is red, yellow, pink and a bit of white,
Put it together and it gives you a fright.

Love smells like Mum's perfume and Dad's aftershave,
Roses and Mum's cooking, hooray!

Love sounds like popping popcorn in a pan
And songs that come from children's hearts.

Love tastes like candy canes on a Christmas tree,
Chocolate bells and sweet ice cream.
It also tastes like toffees, chilli powder and a packet of crisps,
Put it together and you get mince!

Love looks like red hearts and smiley faces.

Love sounds like beating drums
And bubbles popping one by one.

Love reminds me of strawberry jelly and caramel Galaxy.
Oooh, what a treat, and family hugs at night!

Fiona Campbell (10)
Riverside Primary School, Stirling

Sadness

Leaving Dalguise was not easy,
I didn't want to leave,
I was reading every night,
And watching movies too,
Listening to Ozzy Osborne,
The Prince of Darkness,
In the movies with Kenny,
From South Park too.

Sadness smells like rubbish
And burning rubber too,
The colour is black and grey,
It sounds like people screaming and shouting.

Connor Harper (11)
Riverside Primary School, Stirling

I Can't Write A Poem

(Based on 'I Can't Write A Poem' by Bruce Lansky)

See ya later!
You're kidding!
A dog ate my jotter on the way to school.
Aliens took my brain while I was sleeping
And replaced it with a mushy pea.
My hamster ate my pencil.
It's illegal, besides I'm allergic to work.
I am about to fall asleep and I need the toilet.
My work fell into a fire.
Looking at work makes me sick.
I have better things to do.
It's too boring for a fun boy like me.
Time's up? Uh oh!
All I have is this list of dumb excuses.
You like it? Really?
Thanks a lot.

Zack Davidson (10)
Riverside Primary School, Stirling

I Can't Write A Poem

(Based on 'I Can't Write A Poem' by Bruce Lansky)

I'm not writing a poem
Not even for five minutes,
Old people do poems - not young!
I have a headache,
I feel sick,
I'm doing 20 shows,
A Primary 7 broke my hand
And I can't write with my left hand!

Time's up? Uh oh!
All I have is this dumb list of excuses.
You like it? Really?
Thanks a lot.

Kerry McLaughlin (9)
Riverside Primary School, Stirling

Happiness

Orange, ginger, white and red,
You can't be happy without going to bed,
Happiness smells of sweet daisies dancing in the sun,
Just trying to have some fun,
She, Happiness tastes of sweet juicy strawberries,
Never too tasty to have brilliant blueberries,
Happiness looks like children smiling, having fun,
None of them crying out 'Mum',
She feels like bubbles bubbling,
That never stops mumbling,
And she always reminds me of children picnicking,
Mothers holding babies, happy to sing,
I love being happy,
The opposite of crabby,
I wish everybody was happy,
Nobody would be snappy.

Nadia French (10)
Riverside Primary School, Stirling

Anger

Anger is red,
Like a violently erupting volcano,
You feel like you've got a bomb inside you,
Ready to explode,
Anger has the smell of sweat and blood,
Just like you were in a real boxing arena,
It tastes of hot air,
As if you were eating a hot air balloon,
Anger looks like pouring black rainclouds and thunder and lightning,
Just like on a stormy night,
It sounds like banging and crashing,
Just like a building collapsing,
Anger reminds me of World War II,
With all the anger and hatred going around.

Lucas McMenemy (9)
Riverside Primary School, Stirling

Sadness

Sadness is like a rainy day,
Dark clouds and black alleys.
As scary as you can get,
And when you scream
Only an echo of your voice comes back.

Sadness is crying,
Cats screaming and most of all dying,
Sadness is also walking alone lonely at night,
But when you need help no one is there.

Sadness is like a rainy day,
Dark clouds and black alleys.
As scary as you can get,
And when you scream
Only an echo of your voice comes back.

Matthew Crawford (10)
Riverside Primary School, Stirling

Fear

The taste of fear is like chillies and pepper,
It makes you cry and tickles like a feather.

Fear smells like onions and dead roses,
Tickles your eyes and hurts your nose.

Fear looks like a huge dog,
Charging towards you like an angry mob.

It makes you laugh, it makes you cry,
It makes you want to run and hide.

The colour of fear is black and gold,
Dark as night and harsh as voles.

Fear feels like apple bees,
Biting your hair and stinging your knees.

Sharda Smith (11)
Riverside Primary School, Stirling

I Can't Write A Poem

(Based on 'I Can't Write A Poem' by Bruce Lansky)

My hamster peed on my pencil case
And all my pencils in it.
My fish ate my jotter and all the paper in it.
I can't be bothered doing it.
I'm allergic to school.
I don't know what to do.
I stood on my sharpener.
I also lost my thinking cap.
I lost my dinner card and my money.
I got stuck in my room.
The handle is stuck.
I feel sick.
I can't go to school.

Jemma Hammell (9)
Riverside Primary School, Stirling

I Can't Write A Poem

(Based on 'I Can't Write A Poem' by Bruce Lansky)

You must be joking.
My brother snapped it.
My mum put it in the washing by accident.
Someone stood on my pencil.
A monster ate all my pencils.
Someone put my pencil in the bin.
I was sick on it.
Someone drew on it.
Time's up?
Uh oh!
All I have is this dumb list of excuses.
You like it? Really?
Thanks a lot.

Cameron Tahsin (9)
Riverside Primary School, Stirling

I Can't Write A Poem

(Based on 'I Can't Write A Poem' by Bruce Lansky)

I can't write a poem, remember I got in trouble for pulling the alarm,
And I can't write a poem, I've broken my arm,
And I can't write a poem, I work in a farm,
Oh and you said yesterday, we won't be doing any writing.

I can't write a poem, you say I'm a rat,
And I need to feed my stinky cat,
Anyway I need to eat food to get more fat,
And I can't write, I got bitten by a bat.

Time's up? Uh oh!
All I have is this dumb list of excuses.
You like it? Really?
Thanks, I'm the king of poems, yeh!

Kieran Nixon (10)
Riverside Primary School, Stirling

I Can't Write A Poem

(Based on 'I Can't Write A Poem' by Bruce Lansky)

You're kidding!
Aliens took my brain when I was sleeping.
My hamster ate my pencil.
I don't want to!
I am allergic to work.
My homework fell in a bonfire.
Poems make me throw up!

Time's up? Uh oh!
All I have is this dumb list of excuses.
You like it? Really?
Thanks a lot.

I am the best poetry writer in the world.

Louie Johnston (9)
Riverside Primary School, Stirling

Leaves

Leaves are falling off the trees
In the autumn
Brown, gold and orange
They
Twirl
In
The
Breeze

They
Fall
Off
The
Trees.

Jennifer MacPherson (7)
Riverside Primary School, Stirling

Happiness

Happiness smells of sunflowers,
Happiness tastes like chocolate cake,
Happiness looks like a party,
Happiness feels like fun,
Happiness smells like lavender,
Happiness reminds you of sunny days,
Happiness sounds like the sea splashing against the sand,
Happiness is multi-coloured.

Happiness reminds you of Christmas, parties,
Birthdays, Easter, pets and families,
Happiness smells like perfume,
Happiness tastes like lollipops,
Happiness is a sunny day.

Lucy Smith (9)
Riverside Primary School, Stirling

I Can't Write A Poem

(Based on 'I Can't Write A Poem' by Bruce Lansky)

You must be joking,
I've got a broken arm,
My cat used my schoolbag as a toilet,
Someone stole my ruler,
The aliens are still abducting my pencils,
My hamster wrecked my jotter with a truck,
I am actually a ghost!

Time's up? Uh oh!
All I have is this dumb list of excuses.
You like it? Really?
Thanks a lot.
I am the king!

Adam Shaw (9)
Riverside Primary School, Stirling

I Can't Write A Poem

(Based on 'I Can't Write A Poem' by Bruce Lansky)

I feel too sick
My pencil's broken in two
I need the toilet too!
I ripped it in two
My dog ate it
I dropped it in the toilet
My brother stole it
I dropped it in the sink

Time's up? Uh oh!
All I have is this dumb list of excuses.
You like it? Really?
Thanks! You've saved my bacon.

Peter Grayburn (9)
Riverside Primary School, Stirling

Fun

Fun is the colour green,
It makes me feel very light,
Running around playing games,
Fun is the colour green.

Fun sounds like laughing,
It looks like the sun is shining,
You can have fun anywhere,
Fun is the colour green.

Fun tastes like a lovely roast chicken,
It's even better when the sun is shining,
You can still have fun in the pouring rain,
Fun is the colour green.

Elliot Harris (9)
Riverside Primary School, Stirling

I Can't Write A Poem

(Based on 'I Can't Write A Poem' by Bruce Lansky)

You're telling me to write a poem, *no way!*
I have lost my thinking cap!
I accidentally ripped my jotter for my guinea pig's cage.
A hamster went in my ear and ate my brain!
My pencil is broken.
Someone stood on my sharpener and broke it.
I have made a mistake and my rubber doesn't work.
Time's up? Uh oh!
All I have is this dumb list of excuses.
You like it? Really?
Thanks a lot!
I always knew I was good at writing poems!

Rachel Fitzpatrick (9)
Riverside Primary School, Stirling

I Can't Write A Poem

(Based on 'I Can't Write A Poem' by Bruce Lansky)

You think I would write a poem?
No way, Jose!
I can't see - I lost my glasses!
My pencil is broken.
I don't feel well.
I don't do this kind of thing.
It's too early for me.
Time's up? Uh oh!
All I have done is a dumb list of excuses.
You like it? Really?
Thanks a lot!
I can write a poem, *yes!*

Natasa Wilson (10)
Riverside Primary School, Stirling

I Can't Write A Poem

(Based on 'I Can't Write A Poem' by Bruce Lansky)

No way.
I'm having a bad hair day.
You can't be serious.
I fell down the stairs this morning
And I think I've broken my leg.
I miss my finger, honestly my dog ate it.

Time's up? Uh oh!
All I have is this dumb list of excuses.
You like it? Really?
Thanks a lot.

I knew I was always good at writing a poem.

Rebecca Mullan (10)
Riverside Primary School, Stirling

Hope

Hope tastes like ripe, succulent strawberries
covered in a thick runny cream.
It smells of freshly cut grass on a warm summer's day.
It sounds like a stream gently trickling by some rocks.
Hope looks like a field of pure white flowers
blowing in the gentle wind.
It's white like the petals of a newly sprung daisy.
Hope feels like a warm, fluffy blanket
covering a cold baby in his cot.
Hope reminds me of those soldiers
who never gave up during World War II.

Magnus Henry (11)
Riverside Primary School, Stirling

Leaves

Leaves are falling off the trees
Yellow, red, gold, orange and brown
They are twirling slowly
Sometimes fast
Big and small
Twisting down
down
down
to
the
ground.

Fatimah Hamid (7)
Riverside Primary School, Stirling

I Can't Write A Poem

(Based on 'I Can't Write A Poem' by Bruce Lansky)

My jotter fell through the floorboards
Aliens abducted my pencil
I was sick on my jotter
My hamster got a flamethrower and burnt my jotter
My paper fell down the drain
Time's up? Uh oh!
All I have is this dumb list of excuses
You like it? Really?
Thanks a lot!
I am *awesome!*

Jake Davidson (9)
Riverside Primary School, Stirling

Leaves

Autumn leaves of gold and brown
See them swirling to the ground
See them dancing all around
What a sight to see
Such fun as they dance around
Watch as they have such fun
When autumn comes around
They fall to the ground
All colours, red, yellow
Orange, green and bronze.

Zara Hinde (8)
Riverside Primary School, Stirling

I Can't Write A Poem

(Based on 'I Can't Write A Poem' by Bruce Lansky)

I am tired and I can't find my pencil
Also I fell and twisted my arm this morning
I have a headache!
A crocodile stole my ideas
Time's up
All I have is this big list of excuses
You like it?
Really?
Thanks a lot!

Chelsea Ross (8)
Riverside Primary School, Stirling

I Can't Write A Poem

(Based on 'I Can't Write A Poem' by Bruce Lansky)

A horse ate my pencil.
A monkey turned my brain into bananas.
I've lost my jotter.
My head's sore.
A poem! You have to be joking?
Time's up? Uh oh!
All I have is this dumb list of excuses.
You like it? Really?
Thanks a lot.

Madeline Frame (9)
Riverside Primary School, Stirling

Autumn Leaves

Leaves fall down
From my tree
Yellow, red and brown
Drifting slowly to the ground.

George Taylor (7)
Riverside Primary School, Stirling

Leaves

Orange, brown, red and yellow
Softly swirling
Quietly going
Going
Down
Down
To
The
Ground.

Megan Rennie (8)
Riverside Primary School, Stirling

Leaves

Leaves are falling
down from the trees.

There are lots of leaves
falling down from trees.

Golden, orange and brown
falling
falling
to the ground.

Mohammad Sufyaan Abbas (7)
Riverside Primary School, Stirling

Leaves

Leaves of orange, yellow and brown
Tumbling slowly
Twisting and drifting
to
the
ground.

Molly Waddell (7)
Riverside Primary School, Stirling

Autumn Leaves

Orange, red and brown leaves
are falling down,
down,
down.

Falling,
dancing,
diving in the air
And swirling everywhere.

Susanna Keith (7)
Riverside Primary School, Stirling

Joy

Joy looks like people having fun,
It tastes like sweets,
It feels like babies' so soft skin,
It sounds like laughter,
It smells like chocolate cake,
It is the colour lilac, like the petals of a flower,
It reminds me of the look on a mother's face
When she has just given birth.

Caitlin Cardwell (11)
Riverside Primary School, Stirling

Sadness

Sadness feels like a big black cloud hanging over your head.
Sadness smells like burning rubber.
Sadness sounds like thunder cracking.

Sadness looks like dying flowers.
A sad colour is deep blue.
It also tastes like stale bread.
Sadness reminds me of children crying.

Rebecca Lackenby (10)
Riverside Primary School, Stirling

Pain

Pain is when you get hurt really, really badly
It is red because sometimes when you are in pain you could be bleeding
It tastes horrible - like black coal
It smells like sewage rats
It looks like burning flesh
It feels like a splinter in your finger
It reminds me of hurting my toe and having the nail come off.

Dylan McGuire (11)
Riverside Primary School, Stirling

Leaves

Leaves come drifting
Down and
        down
Orange and yellow ones
Drifting
        down
            and
                down.

Melissa Goldie (8)
Riverside Primary School, Stirling

Silence

Silence,
Empty galaxies of nothing,
Breathing echoes and the wind whispers,
Midnight rings as the last train leaves,
Air is the only food - nothing is left,
Clear, gone, vanished,
Wanting something but nothing's there,
Silence.

Alex Mortimer (11)
Riverside Primary School, Stirling

Fun

Fun is yellow like the warm summer sunshine.
It looks like sunflowers.
It sounds of happiness and laughter.
It feels like you want to play again.
It tastes like ice cream and pancakes.
It smells like fresh air.
It reminds me of canoeing and horse riding.
Fun!

April Hanslow (9)
Riverside Primary School, Stirling

Joy Is . . .

Joy is yellow just like the sun.
Happy people playing in the sun.
It smells of fresh air.
Joy is people laughing as loudly as they can.
It tastes like chocolate melting in your mouth.
You can't stop smiling.
It reminds me of when I was younger,
On Christmas morning.

Celine McColl (10)
Riverside Primary School, Stirling

Fear

Fear is red like a hot burning fire.
Fear feels like the scariest horror film out.
Fear smells like hot ash.
Fear sounds like screaming people on a roller coaster.
Fear tastes like the hottest pepper ever.
Fear looks like a volcano erupting.
Fear reminds me of splitting my knee right open with glass.

Lewis Turnbull (9)
Riverside Primary School, Stirling

Fun Poem

Fun is bright yellow.
It reminds me of the time I had good fun.
Fun tastes like good happy days.
It smells like a summer's morning.
Fun sounds like a silent night.
It looks like a bright purple night
And the birds singing.

Leah McCulloch (9)
Riverside Primary School, Stirling

Terror

Terror is red like danger.
Terror looks like a zombie.
Terror sounds like death.
Terror feels horrible.
Terror tastes blank.
Terror smells putrid - like teachers' feet!
Terror reminds me of a film with terror in it called 'Twilight'.

Brendan Bonner (8)
Riverside Primary School, Stirling

Love

Love tastes like a cake.
Love smells like a red rose.
Love reminds me of my dad kissing me.
Love sounds like the fresh air.
Love looks like a bee.
Love feels hot.
Love is pink.

Fionn Henshaw (9)
Riverside Primary School, Stirling

Love

Love is a red, red rose
It sounds like a violin sweetly playing in tune
Love tastes like the finest chocolates in the world
It feels like a mushy marshmallow
Love smells like the most expensive perfume
It looks like the nicest thing you've ever seen
Love is my mum and dad and will be for evermore.

Olivia Richmond-Ferns (10)
Riverside Primary School, Stirling

Friendship

Friendship, golden like a summer day
It sounds like babies' laughter
It smells of blue bluebells
It feels like a kitten's soft warm fur
It tastes of yummy honey
It looks like a beautiful butterfly
It reminds me of a baby smiling for the first time.

Fairlie Glen (11)
Riverside Primary School, Stirling

Fear

Fear is black, like a dark winter's night,
Fear sounds like screeching and screaming,
It tastes like a sour olive,
It feels like rough gravel,
Fear smells of blood and fury,
It looks like a dark, dark night,
It reminds me of horror movies.

Abbi Stuart-Monir (10)
Riverside Primary School, Stirling

Fun

Fun feels sunny.
Fun looks like children playing.
Fun is the colour yellow like the sun.
Fun smells like sweets.
Fun sounds like laughter.
Fun tastes like chocolate.
Fun reminds you of Saturdays.

Ernest Jakub Jurewicz (11)
Riverside Primary School, Stirling

Happiness

Happiness is bright yellow like the sun,
It smells of sweet, fresh air,
It tastes like candy falling out the sky,
It sounds like birds in the sky,
It feels like melting chocolate in your mouth,
It looks like the sun on a bright day,
It reminds you of good times every day.

Abbey Watmore (10)
Riverside Primary School, Stirling

Pain

Pain sounds like a terrifying scream
It looks like blood running down your skin
Its colour is red like blood dripping down your face
It smells like onions
It tastes like a citrus lemon
It feels like you are being tortured
It reminds me of when I fell off my bike.

Cole Harron (9)
Riverside Primary School, Stirling

Fear

Fear is a big black cloud on a stormy night,
It's silent but you can slightly hear teeth chattering,
It's black as fresh coal when it's not been used,
It tastes of salty tears that drip from your eyes like a broken tap,
It reminds me of a nightmare you never want to have,
It feels like you're not going to live,
It smells like liquorice, sour and unusual.

Melissa Hammell (11)
Riverside Primary School, Stirling

Hope

Hope is white like snow,
Hope smells of lavender sitting in the sun,
Hope tastes like warm vanilla pods,
Hope looks like white roses ready to grow,
Hope sounds like butterflies fluttering in the wind,
Hope feels like fluff,
Hope reminds me of happiness.

Alistair Williams (11)
Riverside Primary School, Stirling

Fun

Fun is a bright yellow sun.
It tastes like burgers, chips and pizzas.
Fun smells of candyfloss and toffee apples.
It sounds like children playing in the park.
Fun looks like a colourful carnival.
It feels like you can run forever.
Fun reminds me of going to the sunny beach.

Iona Gibson (9)
Riverside Primary School, Stirling

Leaves

Leaves of autumn on the trees
Yellow, bronze and brown
Dancing and twirling
to
the
ground.

Olivia McGill (7)
Riverside Primary School, Stirling

Leaves

Dancing, twirling, crackling, falling,
drifting, tumbling, circling,
swaying
down to the
ground.

Emily McVitie (8)
Riverside Primary School, Stirling

Rage

Rage is the colour of a fire, red that comes from the pits of Hell.
Rage is a war with endless surrounding of pain and suffering.
Rage is a horrible smell, a stench, a retching, reeking stench.
Rage sounds like screaming anger wanting to be let out!
Rage looks like pain, hate, hurt, it looks like a power bursting.
Rage feels like so much hate that it controls you, you can't stop it.
Rage tastes like uncooked, raw meat.

Jamie Lewis (11)
Riverside Primary School, Stirling

Joy

Joy is a thing that is playful and fun.
White as the clouds without sound.
It has no smell but has a taste of candyfloss.
Joy is a thing that reminds me of playing with my friends.

Tony Godley (9)
Riverside Primary School, Stirling

What Are You Doing?

Why are you picking on me?
Why, why, why?
What have I done to you?
Why are you picking on me?
Why, why, why?

I am scared, I feel exhausted every day.
Because I am trying to get away from you,
I can't stand this picking on me
Why, why why?

What have I done to harm you for you to pick n me?
Do you know what you are doing to me?
I feel scared, frightened, petrified and terrified,
I don't want to come to school because of you.

Why are you always on my back?
Do you want me to get my dad?
Stop it now and I mean it, stop it,
What are you doing to me?

Now I am scared to go on the school bus or any bus because
You are always on one of the buses,
Has someone done something to you?
I think you should stop it now
Why are you doing this to me?

Charese Graham (10)
St Andrew's Primary School, Falkirk

What Are You Doing?

Why are you making my life miserable?
Why is it that you cannot be kind to others?
You are hurting me for no reason at all.
Do you know what you are doing?

It is hurtful and terrible to me.
I can't stand what you do to people.
You're making school a place that I hate, because of you.
Why are you doing this to me?

I feel scared of you, you are very mean and it's
Shocking if you think it is fun to hurt others,
Why do you attack me and mock me?
I have done nothing wrong for you to hate me.

You are acting so immature, do you think it is
Funny for people to have blood all over them?
I think you are acting very shockingly and disgustingly,
Why are you making my life miserable?

If you are nice to others they will like you back,
So why do you pick bullying over friendship?
You hurt others to make yourself look big,
But you are not big at all. What are you doing?

Ross O'Donnell (10)
St Andrew's Primary School, Falkirk

The Stars

I can be bright and cheer you up
I can be jolly but I never feel down
I can think clearly and I glow when I do
I can brighten up your world and see what's not been seen
I can communicate with other things
I can turn your frown upside down
I can be quiet and not make a sound
For what am I . . .?

Bryony Cooper (10)
St Andrew's Primary School, Falkirk

What Are You Doing?

What you doing to me?
I have cuts and bruises all over me,
Why are you doing this to me? I am in so much pain,
Where is your brain? Think before you do things,
What are you doing to me?

I don't like being bullied; it's too much pain,
I need a friend; I am so lonely and hurt,
I am going to tell Miss, she will sort it out,
I don't want to go to school tomorrow all because of you,
I wish you would leave me alone.

'Dad do I have to go to school today?'
'Mum I won't go, a boy is bullying me, I can't take it.'
'Mum and Dad, can't you help? I am just too lonely.'
'Miss the boy is a bully, big and bad.'
Why won't anyone help me please, please help me?

It's all a dream, it felt awful real.
Oh no . . .school! I am going to be late
Oh no . . .I forgot about the real bully . . .
What are you doing to me?
Can't you leave me alone?

Amy Shanks (9)
St Andrew's Primary School, Falkirk

A Moose

I can kill with my horns so long,
My glory is the 'foe death' song,
I can make a quick get away,
Even when my plan goes astray.

Though some kids love me, other are scared,
My zoo keepers have to come prepared,
My antlers are deadly and so are my hooves,
I can pounce through fences, walls and roofs.

Ruaraidh Blackwood (11)
St Andrew's Primary School, Falkirk

What Are You Doing?

Why are you picking on me?
Why do you think you can bully me?
It is not fair that you think you can kick, hit
And say nasty things at me.
Do you know what you are doing to me?

I am too scared to come to school,
I feel empty now that you've hurt me.
Why are you doing this?
Why have you done all of this to me?

Why have you threatened me?
I have done nothing to you.
You do this to me everyday.
Why won't you leave me alone?

Why do you think hitting and calling me nasty names is funny?
Why do you think swearing
And spitting on me is the right thing to do?
Just leave me alone from now on.

Lewis William Watson (10)
St Andrew's Primary School, Falkirk

A Tree

I can be tall or short depending on my name,
Many books have given me fame.

Every season my hair changes colour,
Some being nice, others duller.

In spring I am green, in summer the same,
To turn brown in autumn is my aim.

I can live for years but fall very easily,
Sometimes I'll grow fruit very pleasingly.

I produce the paper on which you write,
But once it's made I vanish from sight.

Daniel McMinn (11)
St Andrew's Primary School, Falkirk

What Are You Doing?

Why are you bullying me? it's very bad.
Are you just trying to make me sad?
But it will not be that,
When I am telling my dad!

Dad, I don't want to go to school
All the boys are bullying me
And they all think it is cool!

Why are you picking on me?
It is not very good
Please stop bullying me!
I am not really in the mood . . .

Mum, I don't want to go . . .
All the boys are bullying me
Why? I just don't know

Yes, you have stopped bullying me . . .

And I am not sad and just for that I am glad!

Sean Favier (9)
St Andrew's Primary School, Falkirk

Ice

I can lie at your doorway with not a sound.
I can freeze your lock and keep you out.

I can kill small creatures and stop your car.
I can also keep you away from the bar.

I hate the sun, he dries me up.
He keeps me still he makes me stop.

It gets hotter and hotter as I fade away.
But remember I'm ice and I'll be back another day.

Nathan Hamill (11)
St Andrew's Primary School, Falkirk

What Are You Doing?

Why are you pushing me everyday?
Why do you want to make me sad?
You are so bad. I have to try to hide everyday
To get away from your bullying.

I don't like being around you.
No one should like you because you're just a bully.
I am sick of bullying.
You push people to the ground and take their money away.

You are just wrong. You are sad and you're a bully.
You should be expelled for all the bad things that you've done to other people.
You go for people after school . . . coward!

'Teacher, this boy bullies everyone,
He has been doing it for weeks,
He pushes people down, he takes peoples lunch money...
No one likes being around him . . .he is such a bully!'

David McPhail (10)
St Andrew's Primary School, Falkirk

A Tornado

I can hurt people
Make you homeless
I am cruel and nasty
I'll come rushing into your villages
I whirl around like a roller coaster
Make you scream and shout with fear
I am angry and mean
I am coming to get you
So you better run and hide in fear.

Chloe Gardiner Harvey (12)
St Andrew's Primary School, Falkirk

What Are You Doing?

Why are you hurting me?
Why do you talk about me?
You hurt my feelings every day!
Do you know what you are doing?

I am bleeding on my knees
I can't stand the way you stare at me!
Does it look like I am happy?
I am scared to come back to school.

Why are you hurting me and not anyone else?
Why do you make fun of me?
Why only me?
I pretend to be sick but my dad sends me to school anyway.

Stop pushing me around
Why are you doing this?
Pick on someone your own size
Just why?

Nino Delrio (10)
St Andrew's Primary School, Falkirk

The Rain

I can tinkle and tapper, I can rage, I can roar
And when I am angry, I can flood Ecuador
I can stay away for ages and make people sad
But when I come back the people are glad.

I can make different noises, I'm quiet or loud
And when I am coming you'll see a dark cloud
I can drift, I can drive, I can float, I can dart
I can choose wisely when I want to start.

Sean Megarrell (11)
St Andrew's Primary School, Falkirk

What Are You Doing?

Why are you picking on me?
Why do you do this?
What have I done to you?
Do you know what you are doing?

I am threatened by you, I feel lonely and lost in the world
Stop and think why you do this!
I am too scared to leave the house
Wonder if you could stop?

What have I done to harm you?
Nervous and frightened, I go to school
Please don't harm me!
Take a look at yourself.

I hate it; I can't go out of the house
Without being bullied
I am petrified, scared and hurt
Can't you see what you are doing?

Claire Winchcole (10)
St Andrew's Primary School, Falkirk

A Spider

I can creep across ceilings and slink up walls
I can shiver one's spine though I'm not very tall
I can frustrate grown men and scare little kids
I am menacing, naughty and packed full of wit
I slip through cracks and scarper from foes
I can dart past your newspaper's deadly blows
You cannot defeat me, I forever will be
For I am a spider, a spider I be.

Jessica Donachie (11)
St Andrew's Primary School, Falkirk

What Are You Doing?

Why are you hitting me and pushing me?
Why are you trying to make me sad?
Is it that you are getting bullied too?
Do you know what you are doing to me?

You are making me feel sad and hurt and lonely
I can't stand what you are trying to do to me
You are doing the wrong thing to me!
Do you know what you are doing?

I feel cold and terrified to get on the bus
Are you angry at someone because they have hurt you?
Or is it that you just don't like me?
Have I done something to hurt you in the past?

Is it because I'm the young one?
Why don't you stop bullying me and get on with your own life?
Do you find bullying me funny?
I find it quite scary and terrifying.

Lewis Conway (10)
St Andrew's Primary School, Falkirk

The Moon

I can swim in lakes without making a ripple,
I can travel the world without making a sound,
I am an expert traveller though I move not once,
I am clear thinking and silent,
I can glimmer and shimmer and glow,
I can dance on your bed and you would never know,
I can stay awake all night,
I have to go but I'll be back, tomorrow!

Clare Campbell (10)
St Andrew's Primary School, Falkirk

What Are You Doing?

Why are you hitting me, kicking me and punching me?
Why do you think what you're doing to me is funny?
Where is your mind? Think about what you have done
Why do you have to bully me?

What is the meaning of all the names and faces?
Why are you making fun of me?
What made you so angry?
Why do you have to pick on me?

I get scared when I go to school.
I worry about the day ahead.
And by the time I've entered the classroom.
I'm covered in scratches and bruises!

When I'm leaving school, people avoid me.
Because all my clothes are ripped and torn.
They think I'm an orphan, with a sick disease.
And say, *'Pewee,* she smells like a dog's dinner.'

Niamh Forbes (10)
St Andrew's Primary School, Falkirk

The Sun

I can dance on your hat
Without you knowing
I can walk on your mat
No dirt left ensuing.

I can make forests blaze
By staring too long
When you're exposed to my rays
You may look wrong.

I can lie in your car
For every day not one night
I'm a very big star
And I'm enormously bright.

I'm made out of gas
In the same place I shall stay
I'm just a big mass
Of what you make everyday.

Euan McKenna (11)
St Andrew's Primary School, Falkirk

What Are You Doing?

Why are you doing this to me?
Why nobody else?
Why pick on me?
Do you know what you are doing?

Now everybody is copying you.
Why oh, why pick on me?
I feel like sinking into the ground.
Do you know what you are doing?

I do not deserve this, why me?
I am broken into a million pieces.
I feel as vulnerable as a mouse.
Do you know what you are doing?

Why call me nasty names?
Why make fun of what I look like?
Do I really deserve this?
What are you doing?

Morgan Maria Wallace (10)
St Andrew's Primary School, Falkirk

What Are You Doing?

Why are you hurting me so badly?
Why did you start hurting me? I did not hurt you!
Why are you shouting at me?
Do you know what you are doing?

I am bleeding and have cuts, I feel petrified of you.
I can't stand you swearing at me.
Do I look like I feel good about this?
What do you think you are doing?

I did not do anything to you.
Stop it please! I am terrified of you, leave me alone.
I am nervous to go to school because of you.

Leave me alone, I am begging you.
Please, please go away.
Stop hurting my feelings.
I can't leave the house.

Cameron Carter (10)
St Andrew's Primary School, Falkirk

What Are You Doing?

What are you doing to me, making me bleed on my forehead?
You're treating me worse than most people in the world,
Threatening me!
Yapping and swearing. I wish people were hearing!

You're breaking my friendship, and my heart
Hitting and spitting, you don't care one bit about me!
You make me feel like you're on God's side and I'm on the Devil's.

I don't even know you and you are bullying me.
You're swearing as well and you look like you're six.

Phew it's just a dream.
I'm glad that I'm OK.
I hate bad dreams, but that was the worst dream in the world.

Kieran Patrick Ferguson (10)
St Andrew's Primary School, Falkirk

What Are You Doing?

Why do you swear at me and flings things at me?
Why do you make fun of me because I am different?
Why do you call me racist things?
Why do you upset other people and make fun of them?

What makes you do these things to me?
Why can't you be self controlled?
What makes you push and kick people into trees?
What makes you punch and spit on people?

I feel angry and upset.
I feel as small as an ant.
I feel very disappointed that you do these things.

Why do you do this to me? I have never done anything to you
You should think about it!
I don't deserve it, why are you doing this to me?
Please, can you think of other people before you do this?

Meisha Turner (10)
St Andrew's Primary School, Falkirk

A Fire

I can be mean and cruel.
I can drive innocent people out of their homes.
I can smother your house in smoke.
I can make devastation round every corner.

I can move fast through forests.
I can cause havoc to towns.
I can be violent to cars sending out an alarm.
I leave destruction wherever I go.

I can burn you to ash.
Then my enemy falls on me.
And when I am flickering I say with my last breath.
'I will get you back sometime.'

Alex Hall (10)
St Andrew's Primary School, Falkirk

What Are You Doing?

Are you picking on me because I am smaller?
Do you have any idea what you are doing to me?
I am really scared of you because you are older than me.
I feel frightened of you. I can't stand you bullying.
You are really hurting my feelings.

I feel terrible. Do you feel miserable inside?
I don't like people bullying. Do you like bullying?
I am getting annoyed. If you keep bullying I will tell.
Please stop annoying me.
All the time you have been bullying everyone.

Why are you always bullying?
Why do you pick on me?
Are you just picking on me because I am smaller?
Do you have any idea what you are doing to me?

Caitlin McPhie (10)
St Andrew's Primary School, Falkirk

What Are You Doing?

Why are you hurting me like this?
Why? Is it because you have been bullied before?
Do you know what you are doing to me?

I am lonely and feel so hurt and sad.
I just can't stand it being this way anymore.
Do you know what you are doing to me?

What have I done for you to be like this?
Have I hurt you or done something wrong?
Do you know what you are doing to me?

I don't like you bullying me
I have very horrible and nasty dreams
I don't like it!
Do you know what you are doing to me?

Jenna Lafferty (10)
St Andrew's Primary School, Falkirk

Leave The Throne

They tell me I should follow a grand, more royal life,
But all I want is to spread my wings
And rid myself of stress and strife!

My mother always told me I was a bad egg, the odd one out.
Now I know that she was right.
Though I will not tell her, cause I know she'd die from shock and fright.

Really, all I want to do is to be a simpleton and all.
I'm also scared I'd miss the luxury,
The parties and those fancy balls.

My father was also wise,
He said I'd turn out all wrong,
Even though he's dead now, If I said it, he'd go 'pong'!

So all I really want is to be an Average Joe,
I want to leave the crown,
The throne, the palace, let me go!

Let me spread my wings and fly, travel, see the world!
Let me follow my whims and my heart!
No matter what my parents say.
Today is the day my adventure will start!

Luca Scarabello (11)
St Francis Xavier's Primary School, Falkirk

War!

War is a dark, mean green,
It tastes of rotten, canned fish,
It smells of burning buildings falling to the ground
It looks like the end of the world,
It sounds like anger
It feels like fire burning through you.

Craig McMenemy (11)
St Francis Xavier's Primary School, Falkirk

They Tell Me I Should

They tell me I should grow up
And see all around
They tell me I should see everything
And drop leaves on the ground.

But I just want to stay
And see birds on my branches every day
So I just want to be small and hide
And feel happy and playful inside.

Rebecca Griffith (11)
St Francis Xavier's Primary School, Falkirk

Kind Kevin, The Monster

They tell me I should hurt
Or be like Scary Mary
I am just useless
I am really not that scary.

I'm the worst monster
And I am really nice
If you hear something under your bed
It will be coming to tuck you in at night.

Jack Traynor (10)
St Francis Xavier's Primary School, Falkirk

The Sun

The Sun,
Bright and glowing
Rising slowly
Like fire in the sky
If only it would come
Out more often.

Jessica Gentleman (11)
St Francis Xavier's Primary School, Falkirk

Sunset

They tell me I should set
And then to face my fear
I'll tackle darkness straight on
Or else I'll surely disappear
But I just want to stay up here
And see familiar sights
Because if I leave this world I know
I'm sure to get a fright.

Samantha Debio
St Francis Xavier's Primary School, Falkirk

Mangoes

Mangoes are cheerful orange
They taste like a tropical burst
They smell like a fresh zumo smoothie
Mangoes look like a tropical island
And sound like waves hitting the smooth sand
Mangoes feel like a lush paradise.

Shaun Cole (11)
St Francis Xavier's Primary School, Falkirk

Fear

Fear is a deep, dark, reddish-black,
It tastes like out of date air,
It smells like filthy food that isn't fresh,
Fear looks like a big, freaky clown running out at you,
And sounds like a swarm of howling screams,
Fear makes me feel weepy and petrified.

Emma McEleney (11)
St Francis Xavier's Primary School, Falkirk

Happiness

Happiness is a mellow yellow
It tastes like a juicy, crunchy apple
It smells like a fruit explosion
Happiness looks like the sparkling sea
And sounds like a singing bird
Happiness makes me feel excited.

Jemma Meikle (11)
St Francis Xavier's Primary School, Falkirk

Senses Poem

Bananas are a mellow yellow
They taste like silky sand
Smell like a summer's day
Look like a banana phone
They sound like silence
Make me feel happy.

Euan Anderson (11)
St Francis Xavier's Primary School, Falkirk

Fear

Fear is a dark red
It tastes like sick
It smells like smoke
Fear looks like hell
It sounds like silence
It feels like falling into a bottomless pit.

Joseph Elliott (10)
St Francis Xavier's Primary School, Falkirk

The Beach

The beach is a pretty sugar pink
The beach tastes like a fresh fruit smoothie
The beach smells like a tropical rainforest
The beach looks like a sunny paradise
The beach sounds like happy children laughing
The beach makes me smile.

Jessica Bryce (11)
St Francis Xavier's Primary School, Falkirk

Cats

Cats,
Soft and furry
Walking gracefully
Like a small shadow
Creeping along the path
If only I had one.

Lucy Ferguson (10)
St Francis Xavier's Primary School, Falkirk

War

War is like futile, vile, dark red
It tastes like damp, thick, gritty mud
It smells like rotting, damp, warm bodies
War looks like madness
And sounds like deep silence
War makes me feel broken.

Aidan Kelly (11)
St Francis Xavier's Primary School, Falkirk

Senses Poem

Sadness is a clear, deep ocean blue
It tastes like salty tears dripping from my eyes
It smells like sour lemons
Sadness looks like a dark grey shadow
And sounds like rain crashing to the ground
Sadness makes me heartbroken.

Morgan McBride (11)
St Francis Xavier's Primary School, Falkirk

Bananas

Bananas are smooth and delicious
They are mellow and yellow
Bananas sit and wait
Like a man waiting for the bus
If only I had a banana tree.

Euan Sharp (11)
St Francis Xavier's Primary School, Falkirk

Boredom

Boredom,
Long and bleak
Talking monotonously
Like falling asleep
If only it would never happen.

Laura Smith (11)
St Francis Xavier's Primary School, Falkirk

Stars

Stars,
Beautiful and bright
Lighting up the world in the blue sky at night
Like a hero saving the day
I just wish they didn't go away.

Eirinn Maguire (11)
St Francis Xavier's Primary School, Falkirk

Space

Space,
Mystical and luminous.
Staying still constantly.
Like a garage full of odd materials.
If only I knew what was out there.

Matthew Kennedy (10)
St Francis Xavier's Primary School, Falkirk

Apples

Sweet and juicy
Small and scrumptious
Like a crunchy crisp
If only they didn't go bad.

Musa Khan (11)
St Francis Xavier's Primary School, Falkirk

My Hero Is My Dad

My hero is my dad
My dad is cool and very smart and good fun
He is my hero because he is the best dad in the world
He is better than my mum and Raegun and Katie.

Craig Lumsden (9)
St Ninian's RC Primary School, Cardenden

My Hero

Selena Gomez is an actress with long black hair
She is in a program called Wizard of Wavely Place.

She has a lovely smile that lights up a room
And her teeth are as white as snow

Selena is my role model because of her fashion sense
She must be a lovely girl if I met her

She is in all the magazines
I'm so jealous of her

But she's a pretty girl
And she'll get far

Selena is a good singer too
I think she's good friends with Demi Lavato.

Demi and Selena have made a movie together
And also a song

With some of her tops she overlaps them it's so cool
I love her with all my heart

I hope to meet her soon
She is five years older than me

If she got hurt I would be devastated
So nothing had better happen to her

On TV she is so relaxed
Unlike me now I'm scared I will muck this up

She's small and slim
I admire her so much

If she stared in your eyes
You'd feel like you want to faint

She's just so cool I don't know what to say
I'm star struck just watching her on TV

Selena Gomez is so cool
She makes the boys drool.

Rhiannon O'Shea (11)
St Ninian's RC Primary School, Cardenden

My Hero

My hero is strong
He is bold
Tries his best to get gold
Trains really hard
Never gives up
He is always on his feet
He likes to keep any beat
He'll try his hardest to beat his opponent
But sometimes it's the opposite
May he fail
May he win
Good mood he stays in
Whatever happens
He doesn't care
He's not a bad loser
My hero he is
Because I hope
To be just
Like him
When I am older.

Ramsay McIntosh (9)
St Ninian's RC Primary School, Cardenden

Who Am I?

I wear a red suit
I work with aeroplanes
I have to wear headphones
And I wear big black boots
I'm not famous and I have a son
I fly aeroplanes
Once a year there is a big finale
And everybody cheers
I work with Chinooks and helicopters.

Rory Gilray (8)
St Ninian's RC Primary School, Cardenden

My Hero

Her hair shines like the sun
As she struts down the catwalk
Her dress sparkles like glitter
In the light.

She has a wardrobe
The size of a house
With jeans, hats, clothes and shoes
I would love her wardrobe to be mine.

She smells like roses in the field
Like the smell of perfume in the air
Yellow puffs on her dress
Beautiful shoes everywhere you look!

She's got a two storey make-up cupboard
It's huge and very cool too!

She's great, she's fun!
Twiggy is my hero
She was a model in the 1960's
I'm sure she had some crazy fun!

Remmi Robertson (10)
St Ninian's RC Primary School, Cardenden

My Hero Poem

My hero is my dad.
He is the best dad in the world.
Because he is my dad.
He is a soldier.
He is a nice man.
He is helpful.
He looks after my family.
My dad is cool.
He has a nice bike.

Jacob Marshall (9)
St Ninian's RC Primary School, Cardenden

My Hero

My hero is one
Of those people
Who work hard.
Streaking into the water
Everybody
Wowing she hits the board
The Olympic gold medal
There's no match for her.
Her cap flattens her
Curls of courage.
Australia is lucky to have her.
Standing on the podium
She's number one.
Being crowned Olympic
Gold medallist 2012
My hero Dawn Fraser
I will praise her always.

Candela Gilfillan-Valle (11)
St Ninian's RC Primary School, Cardenden

My Hero

Elvis is cool
Elvis is nice
Elvis is good at singing
He had nice clothes
He dressed well to look good
But he always did
He played good songs
He sang well
He always got to his concerts on time
He never got into rows
He was always good
Everyone liked him so much.

Aaron Taylor (10
St Ninian's RC Primary School, Cardenden

Chris, My Hero

A hero is someone that you look up to
Someone that has done something special.
A hero is strong, cool and intelligent
My hero is all of those things and more.
He never makes me frown
And he never lets me down.

He makes me smile all the time
And he never gives in, ever!
He can cycle around the track
Faster than a Cadillac.
At the Olympics the three gold medals hung
The nation cheered, but mostly Scotland
They were proud to be top of the table,
And best in the world,
My hero is Chris Hoy
He is the best cyclist in the world!

Scott Salmond (10)
St Ninian's RC Primary School, Cardenden

My Holiday Down Under

I went to Australia for my holidays
It was really, really fun.

The thing I liked most,
Was the very hot sun.

I stayed in a place called Innaloo,
It looked all the same
I also went to Manurah,
To see the movie Fame.

I had lots of Aussie barbies
Which were by far the best
But the worst thing of all was . . .
Scott the pest!

Loren Colliar (9)
St Ninian's RC Primary School, Cardenden

My Hero

My mum is my hero,
Because her rating is nowhere near zero.

My mum is fun
And great to everyone.

She is 33
And also loves me.

Her name is Elaine
She's never a pain.

She's serious at school
But at home she's always cool.

We have lots of fun
But that's because she's a mum.

Jack Smith (10)
St Ninian's RC Primary School, Cardenden

My Hero

Miley is the best
She always sings all the time.

Her hair is long and brown
She is always happy.

She is always funny on the go
I don't know where her anger goes.

She's always got make-up on
She's got curls in her hair.

She sings like a rock star
She sometimes gets her words wrong but I don't care.

She dances like a rock star
She sometimes wears dresses but not a lot.

Alix Barr (10)
St Ninian's RC Primary School, Cardenden

My Hero

He rides across the muddy track
Doing jumps everywhere.
He always overtakes
Here and there
Doing jumps in the air
He is in lots of races and when he wins
It's smiley faces
He wears a suit
That's blue
With a wolf on it too
Zoom, zoom across the track on his motorbike
Hooray, hooray he has won
Off home now
To have some fun.

Reece McMahon (10)
St Ninian's RC Primary School, Cardenden

My Hero Torres

He is fast like lightning, he is a striker.
He is brave, amazing and top goal scorer.

He is like fire, he plays for the reds.
He is a really good player.

He runs up the pitch like lightning.
He got Liverpool to the Championship League.
He scored in the Championship League.
He is good on penalties but sometimes misses.
He is good on shots just like a rocket.
Torres played for Spain.
He is Spain's top scorer.
Spain won the Euro 08 because of him
Liverpool won against Man Utd all because of him.

Liam Roeleveld (12)
St Ninian's RC Primary School, Cardenden

Who Am I?

I live in America
I work on a television show.
I am female.
I work on the X-Factor.
I am very famous.
My last name is Cole.
I was in a band.
Now I just sing by myself.
Me and my band broke up.
I am quite strong.
The first letter in my name is 'C'.
And the last letter in my name is 'L'.

Daria Grieve (8)
St Ninian's RC Primary School, Cardenden

My Hero

My hero is my dad
And his hair is dark brown
It matches his dark boots
Plus his old dark motorbike
He crashed it in the dark
It was his fault
He is my hero
Because I was choking
On a one pound coin
He put me upside down
And it came out
I was sick after it.

Connor Wilson (10)
St Ninian's RC Primary School, Cardenden

Ricky Carmichael

My hero glides through the air like an eagle.
He loves to ride a dirt bike,
My hero belts round the track like a jet.
He likes to win championships.
My personal record breaker.
He has broken the high jump in New York.
The hero loves to impress the crowd.
He has a funny wife who is cute.
My hero can go over 150mph
He is an American dirt bike rider
His wife likes him riding to the extreme
Have you guessed my hero? It is Ricky Carmichael.

Matthew Lindsay (11)
St Ninian's RC Primary School, Cardenden

My Hero

He makes the scouts
He has caught 47 trout
He's an inspiration
To all the nation
Although he's gone
We'll never forget
Now all camps are poor and wet
He started the fun and games
He even let us go on trains
He told us how to build a fire
Sometimes he was a liar.

Ramsay Paterson (11)
St Ninian's RC Primary School, Cardenden

Who Am I?

I was a famous singer.
I wore lots of hats.
My name was Jacko.
I could do the moon walk.
I wore black shoes and white socks.
I wore funky clothes.
I was happy with big crowds.
I had a sister.

Milo Petch (7)
St Ninian's RC Primary School, Cardenden

My Hero

My hero is a cool man,
He is Paul O'Grady,
He makes people laugh
Not like a calf.
He gives people prizes
And gifts and holidays.
He has a dog called Buster
With fluff like a duster.

Ben Fagan (8)
St Ninian's RC Primary School, Cardenden

My Hero Poem

My hero is Lady GaGa.
Lady GaGa never gives up.
Lady GaGa looks fantastic.
Lady GaGa is a fashion icon.
Lady GaGa is very responsible.
Lady GaGa is my favourite singer.
That is why she is cool.

Heather Mercer (9)
St Ninian's RC Primary School, Cardenden

My Hero Is Florence Nightingale

She was a nurse
She was born on the 12th of May 1820
She helped the poor
She was born in an upper-class home
She was a nurse in Japan
She gives me inspiration.

Leah Swan (9)
St Ninian's RC Primary School, Cardenden

My Mum

My mum is beautiful
She is nice and also helpful
My mum is responsible and reliable
My mum cheers me up when I am down
She wakes me up when I am sleeping
I love her very much.

Declan Malcolm (9)
St Ninian's RC Primary School, Cardenden

Samaras

My hero is Samaras
He is very tall
He is also good with the ball
He is popular and scores lots of goals
He is the best of them all
Samaras is dodgy but cool.

Kurt McConville (9)
St Ninian's RC Primary School, Cardenden

Who Am I?

She sings in a band.
Her nickname is GaGa.
She is famous.
She has a big crowd,
When she sings they shout and cheer.
She makes me so happy.

Jordyn Cuthbert (8)
St Ninian's RC Primary School, Cardenden

Who Am I?

I live in London.
I come from the X-Factor.
My name starts with an S.
I am famous.
I have the over 25's on the X-Factor.

Mason McConville (8)
St Ninian's RC Primary School, Cardenden

China's One Child Policy 2009

It's 2009 and the one child policy has struck me hard,
I feel lonely as I look around the
Empty flat where I live, above the smoky city,
Nobody to play with, no children in sight.

When I go to school I feel happy, because my
Friends are there but at home it's the opposite.

I hear nothing except the busy, noisy town outside,
I draw dragons and mythical creatures,
Instead of playing with my mum and dad,
Because I don't think they're very exciting.

Why couldn't *they* start the one child policy after
I got a brother or sister, why? Why? Why?

Tom Paterson (10)
Torrance Primary School, Torrance

Protest In Tiananmen Square 1989

Here I am standing in the square,
Looking around everywhere,
And as I am peering at the protesters,
They are certainly not cheering,
Shouting and bawling is not the way,
That is what the Government say,
'Corruption in China' is what they shout,
I don't see what the problem is all about,
Seven weeks they've been standing here,
Now the Government is in fear,
They send in the tanks and guns,
Now the killing has begun,
A strange man standing in front of a tank,
One second he was there,
The next,
He was not,
These protesters are a sight I will never forget,
Oh, look there's a soldier,
Pointing a gun at my head . . .

Mark Kent (10)
Torrance Primary School, Torrance

The Protest - China 1989

I stood there in Tiananmen Square,
As we protested against the Government,
I could hear tanks,
I felt scared but just kept shouting,
I saw the tanks coming fast,
They were coming near,
I felt the fear,
Unfortunately people were dying,
I was the only one left,
Then no one,
Only death!

Callum Wilson (10)
Torrance Primary School, Torrance

The Escape Of China

I heard that Japan
Is trying to take over our country,
People were taken, cities getting bombed,
People running, we had to leave our city.

I was scared, I was petrified,
Not knowing if I was going to live or die,
My mum said I was not to worry,
But I did, I ran screaming.

We made it to a beach called Wong Song,
We camped under a tree,
My mum said we will make it
To another town or city,

And many days later
We'd passed Shanghi, Xian, Beijing and more,
But we made it, it was amazing.

Sean Alexander Reilly (10)
Torrance Primary School, Torrance

The Protest - China 1989

I lead my class forward.
We are, there, Tiananmen Square.

As we shout and scream, protest and complain.

The tanks come roaring in.

As our shouts grow louder and louder, they get angrier and angrier.

But we carry on shouting, 'Where's the freedom?
Where's the freedom?'

as we shout, we really think we have won.

Then the tank comes closer and closer.

I can see the evil in his eyes. And then we are gone.

Robbie McGale (9)
Torrance Primary School, Torrance

Sadness In China 1937

I walk through the street,
Then I stop.
I hear planes,
Then I see dead people.
Run for your life,
Dead people I see.
I hide,
They know I'm here.
Before I die,
I see someone
Hanging themselves.
I run,
They have spotted me.
Only one
Can survive,
But I was not that one.

Catriona Morrison (10)
Torrance Primary School, Torrance

Untitled

I hate it, just that kind of day,
But where's my brother and sister?
They had to die, but not me.
Just me, standing there worried,
Lonely and sad.
Not the kind of person to be happy,
But sad,
I'm frightened, scared, I'm shouting,
Screaming.
I can't hear anything but the bombs,
I run, I hide, I see someone die.
I can't think of anything else but my family.
That lady lying over there is . . .
My mum.

Naomi Simpson (10)
Torrance Primary School, Torrance

Me In China 1976

I sit here wishing and wishing that,
One day I would no longer be an
Only child!

I just wish I could have someone
To talk to, someone to play with!
Someone to laugh with!

I sit all alone and sad,
Thinking Hu Jintao must be mad!

Am crying,
Am shouting,
Am screaming,
Am feeling sadness in my heart!

I ask myself *why* did the policy
Have to start!

Jennifer Currie (10)
Torrance Primary School, Torrance

China 2009, The One Child Policy

I was sitting there all by myself,
Nothing to do,
It always came back to me,
Why did the Chinese government have to do that?

I mean, why did it have to start in 1979?
Why not in 3000 when I'm dead?
I start to cry,
I try to think of happy stuff, but it just comes back to me.

Sometimes it's great, because my mum and dad take me out a lot,
Like they take me to the funfair,
But when I'm going down the slide,
I'm all by myself, nobody to tell my thoughts to.
Why? Why? Why?

Emma Louise Cameron (10)
Torrance Primary School, Torrance

60th Anniversary

2009 the year of the rabbit,
October the 1st 10:00am the celebrating started in
Tiananmen Square,
I see soldiers marching and dancers dancing along with the parade,

I hear cheers of joy as the parade continuously goes on,
I see people dressed in brightly coloured clothes,
I feel happiness flowing through my veins,

Fireworks soar into the air and sprinkle, swirl, whirl and go *boom*
I see camouflaged tanks all green, blue and white,
I see jets roaring across the sky!

I see beautiful skies all around,
I see the Chinese flag getting raised for the 60th time!
I just know the parade will go to plan,

And that's what happened in Tiananmen Square October 1st 2009.

Robbie Baxter (10)
Torrance Primary School, Torrance

The One Child Policy

I sat in the middle of the room all alone,
I have to play all of my games all on my own,
Every single day I feel so sad.
I can only hang out with my mum and dad.

The one child policy drives me up the wall,
I don't have any brothers or sisters to pick me up when I fall.
Hate, hate, hate being an only child,
But if I had brothers and sisters it would be wild!

Being an only child is so unfair.
I have no happiness I can share.
I wish I had brothers and sisters then I would feel
Like a millionaire!

Amy McShane (10)
Torrance Primary School, Torrance

2093 China's Fear

I feel something's wrong
I wonder what's happening,
I hear people screaming,
I smell gunpowder,
I laugh in worry,
Bang! Bang! The Japanese are here.

I run for my life,
Notice people trapped in their houses,
Then I collapse, I ask myself why I should run,
I am going to die one day, everybody does.

Just then I hear a Japanese soldier behind me,
Getting the ammo ready,
As I am dying,
I sing my favourite song, 'World War III'!

Mhairi-Kirsty Fischer (10)
Torrance Primary School, Torrance

Tiananmen Square 1984

They're coming, I know it,
They'll come and go in a flash,
Still we've got to fight on every little bit,
They've got loads of stashes of weapons and cash.

I see it now, the tanks rolling in,
We'll be surrounded, then be squished,
It's like being trapped in a bin,
I just know we'll be pushed.

Here they come, I see it,
There's a tank we're probably not going to beat it,
Now it's coming closer and closer,
Now I know I'm like squished peanut butter.

Euan Jackson (10)
Torrance Primary School, Torrance

China 1934, Year Of The Dog

I run, away from my village,
I hear, shouting, yelling and crying,
I turn, to see my village one more time,
I see, fire and burnt down houses,
I feel, sad, fear and a tear falling down my cheek,
I turn and run, away from the Japanese.

I hear, the Japanese coming behind me,
I feel, the ground shaking under my feet,
I see, a huge tree right in front of me,
I hide, behind the tree so they can't see me,
I watch, the Japanese run past me,
I stay, until they are all gone.

Sophie Pirrie (10)
Torrance Primary School, Torrance

China, Tiananmen Square

Shouting and bawling, I stand here,
I'm sure the government have given up,
They've had their fun,
As I look at the romantic square,
I hear a steady trundle, then shouts,
I start to shake all over,
They're coming, I know it,
People's thoughts changed,
I'm scared, I don't want to die,
So I start to run, I'll never stop,
I see troops, oh no!
I'm surrounded . . .

Calum Clark (10)
Torrance Primary School, Torrance

China 2009

I Hudintao look at my country,
I see our modern skyscrapers,
I feel happy we're a richer country,
It was hard work to make it better,

I look at Taiwan ungrateful thing,
I notice our lakes, trees and animals,
I see my lovely Tianaman square,
I hear hatched birds singing together,

I think about my people and country,
We will remain rich and wealthy,
China, my country!

Erin Leslie (10)
Torrance Primary School, Torrance

World War II In China 1934

I shout! I cry! As I kiss my mum and dad goodbye,
Off to the train station I go.
I've got no memories except this heart shaped stone.
I'm on my way to China now I feel quite low . . .

I'm in China now, my aunt and uncle are picking me up . . .
It's time for me to start my new school in Beijing,
My red scarf is itching . . .

My first day was OK . . .
It's night time, I've gone for a walk
All of a sudden I see bombs dropping.
They start to get closer and I'm gone.

Helena Anne Murray (10)
Torrance Primary School, Torrance

Lily In China

I can hear a roaring sound,
I can see things in the sky,
I can feel claws on my shoulders,
I look round, it is a dragon
Holding onto my shoulders,
I cry, I shout for help, but
The streets are empty, no one can hear me.
I am really up high,
I fly over waters, rivers and mountains,
I laugh my last laugh,
I fall, I die.

Aimee McKenna (9)
Torrance Primary School, Torrance

The Fall Of Beijing

I hiss, I hiss, I slither through the city.
I hiss, I hiss, I rampage through Beijing,
Destroying everything in my way.

I hear, I hear, the people scream,
The army, attacking me,
I laugh, I laugh, they can't hurt me,
I laugh, I laugh, they can't hurt Sheng Ming (mighty and great).

Then, I hear, I hear a hiss. I hear, I know what awaits behind me,
I turn around, *snap*, I'm gone, another snake has come,
The fall of Beijing has started again.

Ewan McBride (10)
Torrance Primary School, Torrance

China's War

I'm hiding, I hear them, the Japanese.
I can see them, they are getting closer,
I can sense them, their bayonets cutting through the trees.
I am frightened, if they get me, I will be tortured.
I am defenceless and unarmed,
I can smell their presence, the sweat.
They are so close, I can almost see the pupils in their eyes.
I think, I run, a shot, one last breath, I collapse, I die.

Jacob Miller (10)
Torrance Primary School, Torrance

China 1939

I feel them coming,
I hear them shouting,
I see their tanks all about,
I run and hide,
I shout and cry,
I look left and right,
I run and die.

Eve Cameron (9)
Torrance Primary School, Torrance

On My Way To School

This morning, as I was on my way to school,
The world outside started behaving badly.

The cars began to lift up their front tyres and
Charge at me like foxes stalking their prey.
Clouds formed an unhappy face and stared at me,
Making me feel very uncomfortable and unwanted.

As I passed the trees, they threw out their branches,
Trying to claw my eyes out, like wild cats.

Majestic lamp posts stood tall and proud,
Their large eyes following me everywhere I went.

Flags flapping fiercely trying to get free from
The pole, saying, 'Let me go, let me go'.
Strange fences stood like an army trying to
Pierce me with their large points at the top.

A huge aeroplane swooped out of the sky, like a
Hawk trying to knock me off my feet.

Later, things calmed down, but just as I got to the playground . . .
The bell called me into the classroom,
Like my mum calling me for dinner.

Kirstin McLaughlin (10)
Townhead Primary School, Coatbridge

On My Way To School

This morning, as I was on my way to school,
The world started behaving badly.
The cars began to rev their engines after every step
I took, ready to chase me.
Clouds following my every step, waiting for the correct time
To drop a bucket of water on my head.
Walking past houses, their windows like the fierce eyes
of a stalking tiger.
Tall wooden fences standing like soldiers, using splinters as bullets.

The bus came thundering past me, huffing and puffing
its way up the hill.
Majestic lamp posts stood tall and still, watching me approach them.
Long, swaying grass swished its way about, telling me not to
come any closer.

Chugging planes raced across the sky laughing at me every minute.
Trees swayed in the wind, whispering, 'Go away, go away,'
As if they were in a tantrum.
Meanwhile, the bins talked back about me behind my back.
Later, things calmed down, but just as I got to the playground . . .
The bell called me into the classroom.

Colleen Haggarty (11)
Townhead Primary School, Coatbridge

On My Way To School

This morning, as I was on my way to school,
The world outside began behaving badly.
The cars began to moan and groan, as they were stuck in traffic.
The fences stood there, like little soldiers waiting for war.
Big dark clouds were following me getting read to pour huge
Buckets of water all over me.
Bins opened their lids and started to fire rubbish at me,
Trying to make me slip.

Aeroplanes opened their wings like hawks ready to pounce.
I was horrified!
While the lamp posts started walking, following my trail,
As I walked towards the schoolyard.
As I walked past houses, windows looked at me, with fierce eyes.
Trees, with ragged branches tried to grab me
And strangle me until I was blue.

Later, things calmed down, but just as I got to the playground . . .
The bell called me into the classroom.
I was glad that I had arrived safely in the school playground,
But was I really safe?

Jodie Fleming (11)
Townhead Primary School, Coatbridge

On My Way To School

This morning, as I was on my way to school,
The world outside started behaving badly.
The cars began to stand up and quickly roll wheels at me like bowling balls.
As I passed the trees, they started to sway swiftly
And whisper in a ghostly voice, 'Go away, go away!'
Majestically the lamp post stood there tall and bold,
Flashing its light repeatedly, as if it was warning me.
Strangely, the flag flapped about violently like a hawk circling its trapped prey.
Big, dark scattered clouds threw buckets of water at me
And morphed into a scary face that creeped me out.

An aeroplane swooped down quickly as if it was going to gobble me up.
As I walked past the fence, it began to throw skelves at me
As if it was treating me like a dartboard.

Later, things calmed down, but just as I got into the playground . . .
The bell called me safely into the classroom like a comforting blanket.

Aaron Melrose (10)
Townhead Primary School, Coatbridge

On My Way To School

This morning, as I was on my way to school, the
World outside started behaving badly.
The cars began to lift up their front tyres and
Chase me along the pavement.

While trees whistled my name, 'Sarah, Sarah.'
Large white clouds rushed by, making funny faces.
Houses with their eyes like windows
Followed me like hawks stalking their prey.

Lamp posts walking behind me following my every move.
Wooden fences pointing their jags at me
As if they were spears in their hands.
The way the grass swayed it was as if it was
Eating everything alive!

Later, things calmed down, but just as I got to the playground . . .
The bell called me into the classroom.

Sarah Harrison (10)
Townhead Primary School, Coatbridge

On My Way To School

This morning, as I was on my way to school,
The world outside started behaving badly.
The cars began to moan and groan at me as I went by.
Lamp posts followed me as I walked to school
As if they were monsters trying to get me.
While clouds turned grey like they were angry at me.
Buses stood up and began to try and crush me.
Fences tried to jab me as if I was having an injection.
The flags were flapping about like women having an argument.

Later, things calmed down, but just as I got to the playground . . .
The bell called me into the classroom like a security blanket.

Courtney Silvestro (11)
Townhead Primary School, Coatbridge

The Old Town Hall

Never go to an old town hall at night
Or you will have a great big fright.
Lying on the floor right next to the door,
Is a sight never to be seen.

A pool of blood, bright, bright red
And next to it an old silver bed.
I hear a sound,
Very, very slowly I start to turn round.

It's coming from the door,
Up on the very top floor.
As I get nearer,
The sound is getting clearer.

Is it a man?
But, out here at night.
Maybe trying to give little kids a fright.
I get to the top
Slowly I walk closer to the beautiful sound.
Slowly I turn round and guess what I see?

An old grey ghost
With an axe sticking out of his head
Blood trickling down his back, is he dead?
I feel like I'm going to faint,
It smells like fresh red paint.

My head feels like it's going to flood.
The keys are covered in blood.
Very slowly I walk away,
I haven't been there to this day.

Suilven Hunter (9)
Wellington School, Ayr

Marmite

She's a Labrador, a gundog too
With brown shiny eyes
She doesn't let us forget her walk
But if we do we get pawed a lot

Loves her food, swallows it in a gulp
But if she doesn't like the flavour she'll soon
Let us know

Each day she has a crazy hour
And gets a bit carried away

Has a teddy bear and takes it everywhere
Loves it all day and takes it on her walk
Only if she may

I love her a lot without delay
If I didn't have her it wouldn't be the same
When I come home from school she goes inside
And makes me happy every day.

Anna Hammond (10)
Wellington School, Ayr

Imagination

Sit on a chair and close your eyes,
Think of magical creatures,
Dragons, fairies, monsters too,
Think what you want,
It's up to you.

Unicorns dancing to and fro,
Ogres bashing things down below,
Genies making wishes you didn't want,
Mermaids being aware not to get caught.

Don't use concentration,
Just use your imagination.

Holly Martin (10)
Wellington School, Ayr

Scoring A Goal

It was a dark night
The game about to start
Tension in the dressing room
Important that we win

The game started
Our opponents scored
Ten minutes later we scored

In the second half they scored again
30 minutes later we scored again
It was the ninetieth minute
Ball passed to me

I ran past four players
Hit the ball
It was a goal

I ran up the pitch shouting,
'We won!'

Lewis Costley (10)
Wellington School, Ayr

A Sherbet Lemon

A sherbet lemon bright as the sun
Smells like a big juicy lemon
A sherbet lemon, love at first sight

A sherbet lemon, hard to break
When you bite it explodes with flavour
First it goes sweet then sour

When you swallow
You feel robbed
You want to do it all over again.

Matthew Davidson (9)
Wellington School, Ayr

Fairies In The Forest

Walking all alone in the forest at night
I can hear a strange noise but nothing in sight
As I walk closer there is a bit of light
Now I can see some sparkles then I get a fright
I can see a pair of wings, yes that is right
I continue walking, scared what I might find

Walking on a path, leading to a place
That seems so very far away
I can hear voices and I think I saw a face
I put all these things together
And I think fairies are the case

Now I come every single night
To see the fairies glowing with light
They are now my friends
Is there a chance you will find fairies?
You just might!

Courtney McLennan (10)
Wellington School, Ayr

The Invisible Dog

He jumps hurdles
Clean and clear,
Big and bold
What a dog!

Gets called by a whistle
Goes in circles,
Round and fat,
Hates horses and spiders.
What a dog!

Attracted to diamonds,
He walks round town,
What a dog!

Harry Lynch (9)
Wellington School, Ayr

Family

Dad
My dad is number one
He's a pilot and
Wears a special uniform.

Mum
My mum is tall and fancy
Loves shopping for shoes and dresses
Likes a big mystery.

Sister
Far away at uni and
I miss her so much.

Dog
Her name is Crystal
Shiny after her baths
I wish she could talk to me.

Sophie Fairhurst (9)
Wellington School, Ayr

Sweets

Sherbet lemon as bright as the sun
Liquorice bootlace as black as a cat
A hard gobstopper as hard as a rock
Lots of sweets to eat.

Strawberry, blueberry, banana and mint
All these flavours all in one sweet
How do they do it? I really must know
Mysterious recipes to get.

Energetic, sweet, fizzing and sour
It really does amaze me about all these flavours
How they can get them into one sweet
Amazing flavours to try.

Marshall Illingworth (9)
Wellington School, Ayr

Winter Poem

Winter tastes like marshmallows dipped in nice hot chocolate.
Winter smells like people eating hot turkey.
Winter feels like cold snowballs melting on your hand.
Winter looks like a white blanket covering the ground.
Winter sounds like people crunching on the ground.

Daniel McGrath (7)
West Kilbride Primary School, West Kilbride

Winter Poem

Winter tastes like marshmallows dipped in melted chocolate.
Winter smells like turkey on a stick turning on top of a bonfire.
Winter feels like cold, crisp snow on the ground.
Winter looks like melting snowmen.
Winter sounds like sleigh bells ringing.

Matthew McGowan (7)
West Kilbride Primary School, West Kilbride

Winter Poem

Winter tastes like tomato soup.
Winter smells like baked potatoes on a bonfire.
Winter feels like a cold wind.
Winter looks like children having a snowball fight.
Winter sounds like children laughing.

Megan Wilson (7)
West Kilbride Primary School, West Kilbride

Winter Poem

Winter tastes like tomato soup.
Winter smells like hot chocolate.
Winter feels like being cosy in the house.
Winter looks like snow.
Winter sounds like jingle bells.

Megan Bamber (7)
West Kilbride Primary School, West Kilbride

Winter Poem

Winter tastes like fruit dipped in melted chocolate
Winter smells like cooking soup
Winter feels like being shivering cold
Winter looks like shadows walking by
Winter sounds like owls.

Rosie Whitney (7)
West Kilbride Primary School, West Kilbride

Winter Poem

Winter smells like tomato soup.
Winter feels like icicles.
Winter looks like snow.
Winter sounds like Santa's bells.
Winter tastes like turkey.

Lauren McCann (6)
West Kilbride Primary School, West Kilbride

Winter Poem

Winter tastes like hot chocolate.
Winter smells like bonfires.
Winter feels like cosiness.
Winter looks like lightning.
Winter sounds like thunder.

Nicole McCann (6)
West Kilbride Primary School, West Kilbride

Winter Poem

Winter tastes like a cold wind.
Winter smells like hot chocolate.
Winter feels like cold snow.
Winter looks like icicles.
Winter sounds like jingle bells.

Rudi Carrino (7)
West Kilbride Primary School, West Kilbride

Winter Poem

Winter tastes like hot chocolate
Winter smells like burnt bacon
Winter feels like a hot fire
Winter looks like snow
Winter sounds like an owl in a tree.

Gabriella Carrino (7)
West Kilbride Primary School, West Kilbride

Young Writers Information

We hope you have enjoyed reading this book - and that you will continue to enjoy it in the coming years.

If you like reading and writing poetry drop us a line, or give us a call, and we'll send you a free information pack.

Alternatively if you would like to order further copies of this book or any of our other titles, then please give us a call or log onto our website at www.youngwriters.co.uk.

Young Writers Information
Remus House
Coltsfoot Drive
Peterborough
PE2 9JX
(01733) 890066